PSL Book of Model Railway Wiring

# PSL Book of Model Railway Wiring

## C. J. Freezer

Patrick Stephens Limited

The details in this book are to the best of the
author's knowledge and belief both accurately
described and safe. However, great care must
always be taken when assembling electrical
equipment, and neither the publishers nor the
author can accept responsibility for any accidents
which may occur

First published 1989
Reprinted 1991, 1993, 1994 and 1997

British Library Cataloguing in Publication Data

Freezer, C. J. (Cyril John), *1924 –*
 PSL book of model railway wiring.
 1.  Model railways, Electronic equipment.
 Circuits. Construction, — Manuals
 1.  Title
 625.1'9'028

 ISBN 1-85260-173-6

Patrick Stephens Limited is an imprint of
Haynes Publishing, Sparkford, Nr. Yeovil,
Somerset, BA22 7JJ.

Printed in Great Britain by
Hillman Printers (Frome) Ltd.

10  9  8  7  6

This book is dedicated to the many members of the Model Railway Club who, in telling me what they wanted explained, have determined its final form.

# Contents

# Introduction

Model railway wiring is a very simple, straight-forward business: so simple that anyone with a smattering of electrical know-how can work out the fundamentals from first principles. There is nothing particularly esoteric about any part of it, and once one has grasped that it is largely a matter of applying a few simple rules, and a few equally simple circuits, repeated as often as necessitated by the layout in question, all is well.

A lot of trouble arises because beginners so often see, at exhibitions, a large layout controlled by one of the more complicated systems and either believe that all this is essential, or simply decide to copy what they have seen. In the special field of exhibition work, certain advanced techniques are worthwhile, and large commercial layouts are automatically controlled because it would cost too much to employ human operators. Elaborate club layouts are frequently run from a centralized panel because there are so many operators at peak times that it is feasible to have one or two highly-experienced individuals acting as control, whilst the rest drive the trains. When staff is short, one man can keep things moving for the amusement of the public. We then get what is irreverently termed 'the Mighty Wurlitzer'.

The home layout is different. The object is to operate a miniature railway system, which means that the owner gets most fun from working the points and signals, and controlling the trains himself. There is scope for some degree of automation and track circuiting, but, as I shall ex-plain, it is limited by one simple fact: the majority of home layouts are simply not suited for full automatic control. For most of us, wiring should be a means to an end, not an end in itself.

The end is the accurate simulation of the working of a full-sized railway system. This, more than scale accuracy or exact representation of a narrow area of the prototype, is the real objective of the majority of railway modellers. We want, not to play trains, but to copy the workings of the prototype as faithfully as possible. Whilst this might appear to demand a large system, with dozens of stations and as many operators to keep it all running, it is well within the reach of a single enthusiast working in a small space on a fairly restricted budget. Sensible electric circuitry is an important aid towards this objective.

However, the main thing is to get down to the business of wiring the layout. In my experience, more people get into difficulties trying to understand the subject from a theoretical angle than in any other way. You learn to wire a model railway by wiring a model railway. There is no substitute for hands-on experience, and so, more than anything else, this book is oriented towards the practical subject of hooking wires from a control unit to a layout, through a switchboard.

I am avoiding all but the most elementary aspects of electronics, for several reasons. The most important is that the subject has been adequately covered by Roger Amos in books published by Patrick Stephens. I shall where appropriate refer to these as *Amos*.

The second reason is that, as Roger Amos points out, electronic engineering is continually developing, and resembles the White Queen's race in that one needs to run very hard simply to keep up. Although some devices I describe in this book are relatively modern, they are exactly the same in principle as those that were on the market in 1933, when I first took a practical interest in the subject. In those days, the most advanced electronic device was the pentode valve.

A third reason, also mentioned by Roger Amos, is that electronics are very seductive, and one can all too easily end up spending 90 per cent of one's spare time exploring the potential of the microchip, instead of getting down to the business of building a model railway. If there is a better reason for avoiding electronics on a model railway, I've yet to find it!

There undoubtedly are places around a layout where electronic devices have their uses. Luckily, specialist manufacturers are now offering 'black boxes' which only need connecting to the tracks in accordance with very simple instructions. In my opinion, the majority of railway modellers should aim for the 'black box' approach. This is an electronic term for a collection of devices wired within a box, which may or may not be black. The user simply connects the appropriate terminals and cares not what goes on inside the device. It isn't necessary to know, any more than one has to master the principles of thermodynamics to be able to drive a car.

Inevitably, some readers will consider I am explaining the obvious, and labouring long over things 'everyone knows'. The trouble is, everyone does not know. I was in my late twenties before I discovered exactly what was meant by the raucous call of 'Offside ref!' at football matches. It isn't that the offside rule is that arcane; simply everyone assumed I knew and I didn't pluck up the courage to ask until I met a charming girl who supported Southampton FC. Every subject has a private sub-set of the English language and, if you are unused to the field, some of the terms are strange but they must be mastered. I will try to explain the technical terms, but to make certain I am including a glossary. It is also necessary to use schematic wiring diagrams, which are not too difficult to read; at least, the ones in this book aren't over complicated. Again, I shall provide a key, but in the end you must learn the meaning of the symbols.

Model railway electrification is, I will repeat, not a difficult subject, nor is it particularly hazardous. Model railways employ low voltage electricity which is completely safe. Under certain circumstances, however, it can damage electrical equipment, and although the circuits and devices described have been tried and tested, neither the author nor the publishers can accept responsibility for faults caused by inexperience or a simple failure to follow instructions.

Furthermore, it must be pointed out that a hot soldering iron, or any metal object that has been in contact with a hot soldering iron, can cause burns to the unwary, whilst also causing serious, irreversible damage to any plastic part with which it comes into contact.

Finally, unless any mains-operated equipment is correctly wired to a plug, and the mains socket is connected to the supply by approved methods, it is potentially lethal. *If the reader has any doubts as to his own ability, he should consult a qualified electrician when dealing with the mains electricity supply*.

# CHAPTER 1

# Making a start

The best place to start is always at the beginning. Which in this case involves getting a locomotive to move under its own power on a length of track. To do this, we have to get electricity to the motor.

The majority of model locomotives require a specific type of electricity. We call it 12 V dc, and get it from a box of tricks called a power unit. This has a length of mains cable ending in a fused three-pin plug, and at least two output terminals or sockets which are marked either 12 V, 12 V dc, or more explicitly, TRACK. You take two wires, connect one end of each to these output terminals and the other ends to each end of the rails. There may, in addition, be another pair of output sockets, providing 16 V ac for auxiliary power.

There is also a speed control knob which will have an 'off' position either in the centre top, or on the left-hand end of the traverse, in which case there will be an additional reversing switch associated with the knob. These devices control the speed and direction of the train. Yes, I realize you're probably well ahead of me, but as I said in the introduction, I shall often be talking about things that 'everybody knows'.

In Fig 1.1 we have the fundamentals of model railway wiring, a power unit, a length of track, a locomotive (shown in skeleton form) and a pair of wires to link the power unit to the track. Place the locomotive on the rails, plug the unit into a wall socket, switch on, turn the control knob, and off we go.

Of course, if we only have a plain length of track, the locomotive will soon run off the end, so we'll turn to the basic oval of track, which is the starting point of the hobby. At least, it is for most of us – or were you one of the deprived minority who never had a train set? This arrangement is shown in Fig 1.2, but in place of the pictorial isometric drawing we have a schematic diagram, which is slightly easier to read. Fig 1.3 takes this a stage further, showing the two rails as a single thick line, eliminating the loco, which we assume is somewhere on the layout, omitting the power unit, which we know we have to have, and leaving just the two symbols for feed and return. This is a convenient way of introducing a system of simple symbols which I have used for over thirty years to show basic sectionalizing on a layout plan.

The important thing to get used to is the feed and return concept. Forget positive and negative, since every time you reverse, you change the relative polarity of the rails. The rule, as shown in Fig 1.4, is that, facing the direction of travel, the right-hand rail is positive. As a result, all trains go the same way when you turn the controller knob in the appropriate direction. We can now stop worrying about polarity until we brush against electronics in later chapters.

We are, of course, dealing with the two-rail system, which is simple, effective, virtually trouble-free, and now nearly universal throughout the hobby. The rails are insulated from each other to provide the conductive paths, while the

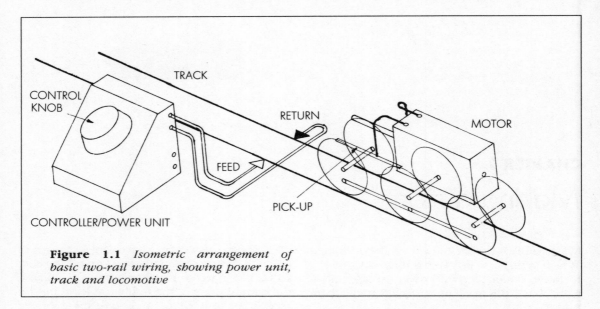

**Figure 1.1** *Isometric arrangement of basic two-rail wiring, showing power unit, track and locomotive*

locomotive, and all the stock, will have insulated wheels. Since this is not a treatise on locomotive, coach or wagon construction, we shall assume that we have on hand a plentiful supply of suitable equipment, ready built, tested and ready to roll. All we need to remember is that the locomotive has some means of collecting the current from the wheels and taking it to the motor.

Before we go any further, there is one very important matter to consider. Not only did I speak glibly of plugging the power unit into a wall socket, I also said that the mains lead terminated in a three pin plug. This is not necessarily so, for a fair proportion of British electrical equipment is supplied without a plug. The first thing to do is to fit one. This is not too difficult, since the unit will be double insulated and the cable will have only two wires, one brown (live), the other blue (neutral). To fit these to a standard 13 A fused plug, first remove the plug's cover, then loosen the cable clip. The live lead goes to the fuse terminal on the right, and the neutral to the left-hand leg of the plug. The top (earth) leg is not connected, since there is no earth (green/yellow) wire on a double-insulated device. Fit a 3 A fuse, tighten the cable clamp, and replace the top. Study Fig 1.5 for clarity; this shows the full wir-

ing with a three-core earthed lead. If you are in any doubt, get an experienced electrician to wire it for you. Better safe than sorry.

We now hit a major snag, since the unit will almost certainly have a lead only two metres long, which is rarely long enough to reach from the layout to the wall socket. This has led to more dangerous extensions being made than I care to think about. The best solution is to buy an extension lead with a four-way socket that is long enough to allow you to carry the lead from

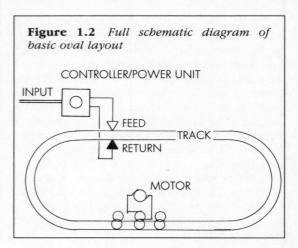

**Figure 1.2** *Full schematic diagram of basic oval layout*

the wall socket to directly under the layout, without passing over any gangway. Why four sockets for one power unit? Well, for a start, you're going to need to plug in a soldering iron, you may also want to use a power drill and a vacuum cleaner. Sooner or later you will also need a second power unit. The extension lead will cater for all this, and provide a further outlet for layout lighting. There are other ways of wiring the unit to the mains; this happens to be the easiest and safest for the veriest newcomer.

We shall now take a more detailed look at the power unit itself, which is the heart of the system. Whilst, for the most part, we will in future treat this as a black box, and concentrate our attention on what happens on the layout side of the output terminals, natural curiosity leads one to wonder just what goes on inside the box. Since it is relatively simple, there is no reason why we shouldn't investigate the power unit.

First of all, I must clear up a common misconception. There is a tendency for the power unit to be called a transformer, an error compounded by certain manufacturers, specifically Continental firms. Agreed, a power unit transforms the 240 V ac mains supply to the desired 12 V dc we need to operate a model railway, but in electrical parlance, a transformer is a static device for changing the voltage of an ac supply. Our power unit contains a transformer, which comprises a quantity of wire wound

**Figure 1.4** *Direction of travel convention for two rail locomotives*

around an iron core. It has an input, or primary winding which is connected to the mains supply, through the 3 A fused plug and mains cable, and one, two or more outputs, or secondary windings, which supply low voltages, generally 16 V ac. It has a power rating which is given as so many va. This rating is derived by multiplying the nominal voltage by the maximum amperage and is a rough equivalent of wattage; the difference is bound up with some of the esoteric features of ac supplies, which need not bother us here.

A basic power unit will usually have a power rating of no more than 12 va, sometimes as little as 9 va. This last is enough to operate a single train on an OO gauge layout and no more. More powerful units have not only a higher rating on the 12 V dc circuit, but an additional 16 V ac output of at least the same rating as well. Some units have two controllers and two 12 V dc outputs, and appear useful, but they can be rather limiting as the model develops. They are mainly intended for the developed train set oval, as shown on

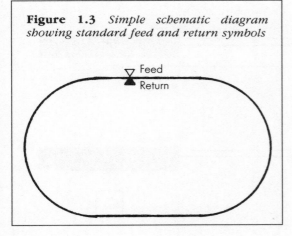

**Figure 1.3** *Simple schematic diagram showing standard feed and return symbols*

Feed
Return

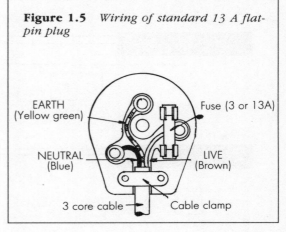

**Figure 1.5** *Wiring of standard 13 A flat-pin plug*

EARTH
(Yellow green)

Fuse (3 or 13A)

NEUTRAL
(Blue)

LIVE
(Brown)

3 core cable

Cable clamp

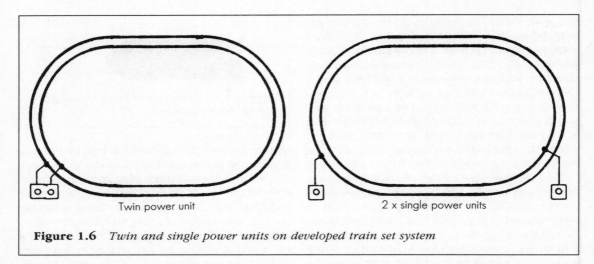

**Figure 1.6** *Twin and single power units on developed train set system*

the left in Fig 1.6, but even here I feel that two single units are better, since this, as shown on the left of the diagram, allows the controls to be separated. The reason for this becomes obvious the moment you allow two children to play with a layout with a twin power unit. Controllers need to be far enough apart to allow two people to stand side by side in comfort and reach the knobs without getting in each other's way.

The disadvantage of the twin unit is more obvious when we consider a more advanced model railway, where we have two termini separated by a length of track. In the upper diagram in Figure 1.7 we show how the twin unit will always be inconvenient for at least one station, whereas with two units the controls can be at each end of the model.

Let's return to the unit and look at the output terminals. These may either be sockets or screw connections. The former are more common, the latter slightly more convenient, provided the nuts have not been lost. Using sockets is largely a matter of getting hold of suitable plugs, or just pushing a wire in and wedging it in place with a

**Figure 1.7** *Twin and single power units on point-to-point layout*

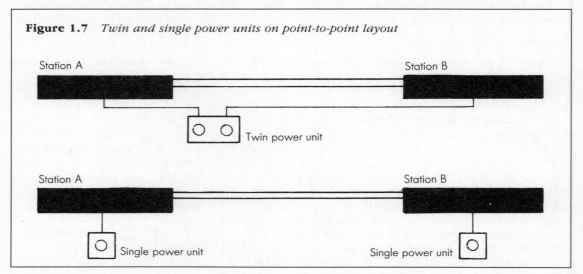

matchstick. On low voltages this bodge is quite acceptable.

The auxiliary 16 V ac is connected directly to the secondary winding of the transformer, and rarely if ever has any internal protection. Its use will be covered in later chapters.

Although the controlled output is often marked as being 12 V, in practice, the voltage you would measure across the rails, if you fitted a meter, would range from around 16–18 V with no train on the track, to around 4 V when running at bottom speed with a normal motor. Locomotives fitted with high-efficiency coreless motors can move at around 2 V, a fact that can make controlling a mixed stud a trifle difficult. There are some advanced controllers around which can compensate for this, but as this is more a question of locomotive design than layout wiring, we shall proceed to ignore it in future.

The knob on the front of the unit controls the speed. It may do so with a resistance, it can do so with a variable transformer, or it can employ electronics. There is a growing tendency to use electronic controllers today, partly because it is easier to add useful refinements, partly because it is now slightly cheaper to make an electronic controller than a straight resistance unit. Furthermore, some electronic controllers maintain a constant 12 V across the track, but chop it into tiny packets at 50 Hz, in other words, 50 pulses of electricity each second are sent to the loco, the length of each pulse determining the speed. This is a very basic description of chopper control, which is also employed on full-sized electric locomotives.

As I mentioned earlier, to reverse the dc motor fitted to most model locomotives you merely have to reverse the polarity of the rails. This is done by a switch, which may be separate or may be combined with the speed control knob.

If I've left you a little bewildered by this dive into technicalities, don't worry. Although various manufacturers and even more amateurs have extolled the virtues of certain types of controller, my own experience over some thirty years of testing is that there is more practical difference between two 'identical' controllers from the same manufacturer than between

high-quality controllers of radically different designs. Most of the claimed improvements in performance for radical developments are arrived at by the standard method, comparison with a second-rate unit. As you will not be dissecting your controller (at least, I strongly advise you not to do so), it is unimportant how the knob controls the speed, just as it is unnecessary to understand the working of a four-stroke engine and a synchromesh gearbox to know how to drive a car.

All decent power units contain some form of current-limiter or cut-out on the controlled circuit, to prevent an overload causing any damage to the unit. It is always possible to do damage to equipment by overloading, and regrettably this can happen all too easily to locomotive motors. It is not a good idea to wait for the loco to send up smoke signals to announce its distress: if it runs sluggishly on full throttle, or worse still, stops dead with the power still on, switch off and check before you do any permanent damage.

The main reason why a cut-out is required is that it is all too easy to create a short circuit on the track. Generally some metal object, usually a pin, screw or nut, drops in the one place where it is least convenient. It is a tedious business ferreting around to find it, but it is better than the permanent short circuit that arises through a mistake in wiring. Even on our simple basic circuit we must make a distinction between the two wires from the unit.

I prefer to describe them as feed and return: simple, unambiguous and, best of all, plain English. Clearly, if you connect one to the other, you feed directly into the return and stop anything else happening. There are various ways of minimizing the possibility of this occurring as you wire the layout, but as expert layout wiremen continually manage to cross their wires, you shouldn't worry if you do it now and then. A large part of this book is devoted to the business of keeping them apart.

At this point we meet our first three rules:

**RULE 1**  Take each feed independently to the layout, via a switch.

**RULE 2**  Join all returns together.

**RULE 3**     Never allow feed and return wires or rails to touch.

We shall meet more rules as we go through the book, and find them all together in Appendix 1.

As I implied earlier, you have probably already got this far, for we have only covered the way a basic train set oval is connected to the power unit. At this juncture the newcomer invariably asks, 'How do I control two trains on one track?' He is often told he will need elaborate electronic devices, simply because he said 'track', whereas he should have said 'layout'. He probably has enough sense to realize that if you put two trains on one simple train set oval, they must go in the same direction at approximately the same speed (which they will do, providing the power unit is able to supply enough current to work them both), or they will collide. If you want to play trains in this fashion, there is a very simple dodge, shown in Fig 1.8, which provides a means of appearing to control two trains independently on a plain oval track.

What we have is a length of track isolated from the main oval and fed through a normally on push-button which is bridged by a low value resistance of around 5 ohms. This, in practice, would be a small coil of resistance wire fitted across the terminals of the push-button.

It is implicit in two-rail wiring that trains always move in the same direction, i.e., with the

right-hand rail positive. However, even if you have two identical ready-to-run locomotives hauling identical trains, one will almost certainly be fractionally faster than the other and will, after a couple of revolutions, begin to catch up on the other. As the faster train passes over the slowing section, the operator jabs the button, whereupon the extra resistance in the circuit slows the faster train, so the other begins to gain.

This is just an amusing gimmick more suited to an exhibition layout than to a serious model railway. I have introduced it at the outset to illustrate an important theme of this book: that, with a little foresight and some low cunning, you may appear to have independent control of two or more trains on the same circuit, without having to use anything more advanced, or costly, than some wire and switches.

In the main we can have two or more locomotives on one layout, whilst ensuring that only one will run at any given time. Alternatively, however, it is pleasant to be able to operate two trains, running in different directions, around the complete system. To do this we will first of all need a layout with sidings, loops and enough main line to allow two trains to run independently of each other. Double track is the most straightforward arrangement, in which case a controller feeding each circuit will give two trains under independent control. We will also require a lot of wire, a number of switches and some other gadgets, all fairly simple and straightforward, so before we get involved in how to connect the lot together, we should first look at what is needed to perform the task.

Before I go any further, I'd like to clear up a small point in my opening paragraphs, concerning those locomotives which do not run on 12 V dc. Some operate on different voltages, but the relative newcomer, who is most in need of this book, is unlikely to encounter 24 V dc locomotives, though he could come up against 9 V dc, since many 9mm narrow-gauge locomotives are set for this voltage, as are all Marklin Z gauge (6.5mm gauge) machines. As Marklin provide special power units, the latter is unlikely to give trouble, but what of the narrow gauge? Well the simple answer is that you can use a normal power unit. If you turn the controller on full, the

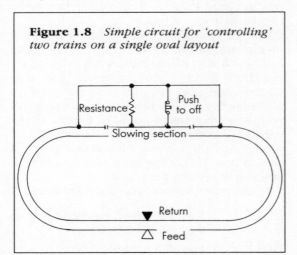

**Figure 1.8** *Simple circuit for 'controlling' two trains on a single oval layout*

Resistance    Push to off

Slowing section

Return

Feed

locomotive will emulate a rocket, which is not quite what we want. If you keep this up for any length of time – and something well in excess of fifteen minutes is indicated – you will overheat the motor and ruin it, but in practice the train comes off the track first. When the speed control is turned down to get the locomotive to run more realistically, the actual track voltage may be no more than 6 V.

I must also mention Marklin HO and Gauge 1, which work on 20 V ac. Once again the correct power units are provided, but as Marklin HO also uses stud contact centre pick-up, rather than the universal DC, it's very much the odd man out. It is not very common in Britain and I fancy that the small, stalwart band of Marklin *aficionados* are well acquainted with the special quirks of the system.

# CHAPTER 2
# Essential equipment

It is rather surprising to discover just how little equipment one needs for wiring a model railway, and how much of that is very basic elementary fittings. Regrettably, the days when you could buy all the essentials in Woolworths are no longer, but most of what you need can be found in any half-decent electrical supply store. I shall have something to say about where to purchase supplies in an appendix; for the moment let's look at what is needed.

## Wire

You don't get very far without wire; in point of fact, you need large amounts of it. You can, if you wish, purchase 'layout wire', neatly coiled in about two metre lengths, but the most economical method is to buy a 100m coil, in any colour you fancy.

Although Woolworths no longer sell single bell wire, they do have twin bell wire, though it is no longer rated as such. The packaging carries the warning that the wire is unsuitable for mains voltages, which is OK so far as we are concerned. It is probably the best source of suitable wire on the high street.

You should never use sheathed mains cable for layout wiring, since it is all too easy to mistake a lead carrying potentially lethal 240 V ac for one carrying innocuous 12 V dc at a moment when you're wielding a pair of wire cutters. However, twin flex, which is rarely used for mains voltages today, can be very useful for layout wiring, particularly where the wires need to bend.

The very heavy 1 or 2.5mm cores from flat mains cable, plus the bare copper earth wire are also excellent for carrying heavy currents, or should you need to run a low voltage lead some distance, on a garden layout, for example. Providing they are stripped from their sheathing and used in such a manner that they are not likely to be confused with mains-carrying leads, all is well.

Multicore cable has its uses, and, to a limited extent, flat ribbon cable can be employed on a layout. The main objection is not so much cost, but rather that it is unusual for the ready-made cable to have the right number of cores, hence one tends to waste a sizeable proportion of a fairly costly item. Of course, this does not apply if scrap multi-cored cable is available at low cost.

## Switches

Although almost any type of switch could be used for model railway control, size and convenience narrow the field to a few main types.

### Toggle switch

This is the basic panel-mounting switch, and comes in two varieties, the miniature and subminiature pattern. The choice is yours; the subminiature certainly makes for a neater looking panel, but I feel a lot depends on how much they cost.

There are several basic types which are denoted by initials:

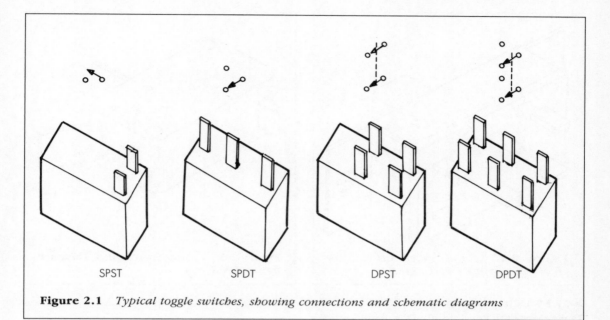

**Figure 2.1** *Typical toggle switches, showing connections and schematic diagrams*

SPST     Single Pole, Single Throw
            The basic on/off switch
SPDT     Single Pole, Double Throw
            The elementary changeover switch
DPST     Double Pole, Single Throw
            Used for isolating
DPDT     Double Pole, Double Throw
            Used for reversing switch and as a
            selector switch
(See Fig 2.1.)

*An array of switches.* **Left:** *sub-miniature toggle*
**Centre:** *miniature toggle* **Right:** *slider.*

Both the SPDT and DPDT switches are obtainable in two versions, the common two position and the less common but rather more useful centre-off type.

### Slider switch

Slider switches generally come in SPDT and DPDT patterns, and are usually cheap and fairly compact. However, they are beasts to fit, as a long rectangular hole has to be cut, whilst they do not take happily to switching heavy currents and, unless they are operated only when the current is off, can prove unreliable in time. (See Fig 2.2.)

### Rotary switch

Sometimes termed a wafer switch, this consists of one or more flat rotary selectors mounted on a common arm. Various 'ways' are available, from 2-way to 12-way, each position being, on the normal pattern switch, at 30 degree intervals. These switches are extremely useful for selecting routes and allocating controllers to specific sections. They can also be used for point operation, providing specific types of point motor, incorporating a cut-off switch, or relays are used.

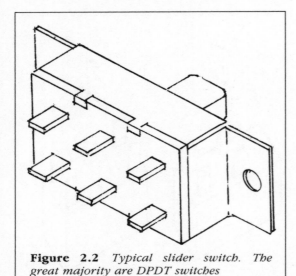

**Figure 2.2** *Typical slider switch. The great majority are DPDT switches*

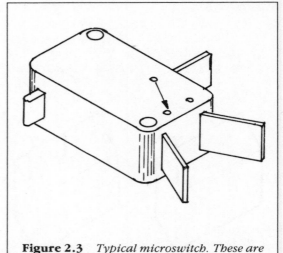

**Figure 2.3** *Typical microswitch. These are mostly SPDT types*

## Key switch

The telephone key switch is a trifle difficult to track down, but with its multiplicity of contacts and the fact that, in general, it is a three-position switch with a very neat appearance, it is an invaluable control switch. Only obtainable ex-equipment, it remains, after years of use, a very sound device, rugged and indestructible, barring the application of extreme brute force.

## Push-button

There are two patterns of push-button, the common push-to-make and the less common push-to-break. The former are employed to energize circuits momentarily, the latter are mainly employed to break latching circuits, of which more in a later chapter.

*PO pattern telephone switches.*

*A pair of microswitches being used to change polarity of point frogs.*

## Microswitch

The microswitch is a flat precision changeover switch, actuated by a very small movement of a trigger. It is totally enclosed and hence the contact is excellent. It has innumerable uses on and around a layout, the most important of which is providing changeover contacts for live frog points. (See Fig 2.3.)

There are other useful devices for control panels, which are best regarded as optional extras rather than vital components. They add to the fun, they certainly impress the visitor, but they also increase both the cost and the work involved.

## Variable resistance

Variable resistances come in a variety of forms, some with rotary motion, some with sliding motion. There is also a distinction between carbon tracks, generally for the higher values and wirewound, which are needed for model railway speed control. Even so, we require heavy duty types capable of carrying a couple of amps, and today these items are quite expensive. (See Fig 2.4.)

## Indicators

A variety of panel-mounting indicator lights are available, ranging from quite elaborate types taking small lamps, to the relatively small and simple light-emitting diode (LED). The latter take little power, are easily secured in a drilled hole with a spot of glue and, providing you fit the correct dropping resistance, will work off any low voltage ac or dc. Yes, I know most authorities quote dc, but a diode converts ac to dc! LEDs often come in interesting shapes, but are only available in a decent red, a washed-out green, and a rather peculiar muddy yellow.

## Neons

The neon indicator is strictly a mains voltage device and is used to show if power is applied to circuit or not. When wired and working it has two bare and live tags at the back, so it is only for the experienced and *must be fitted inside a secure case*. It is, I think, an essential fitting for any mains-powered device, though most manufacturers and the regulating bodies hold a different view.

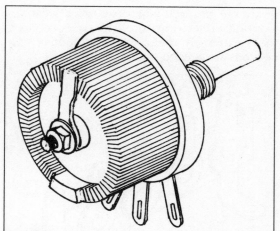

**Figure 2.4** *Typical wirewound variable resistance, high power rating pattern, suitable for model railway speed control*

## Meters

The value of a volt or ammeter on a control panel is, I think, questionable. Certainly, modern electronic controllers, which have a couple of indicator LEDs to show that power is on, and whether or not there is an overload, provide all the essential information on a control circuit. In practice, hardly anyone has time to look at meters. They do look impressive, however, and if some suitable instruments come your way, by all means include them.

The value of a pair of meters on a workbench rig is beyond question, since one is frequently helped to diagnose trouble by their readings.

The following devices are not easy to classify, but are extremely useful on a well developed model railway.

### Tag strip

Whilst it is perfectly possible to wire a layout without tag strip, it is almost impossible to modify the wiring afterwards. Tag strip is reasonably priced, but of late has been a trifle difficult to track down. (See Fig 2.5.)

### Connectors

There is a wide selection of connectors on the market, the most common being the 'chocolate strip' screw pattern, generally sold in blocks of twelve. If you go to a DIY shop and buy it in a pretty bubble pack you'll pay twice what you would at an electrical store. This type of connector is extremely useful where temporary connections are needed.

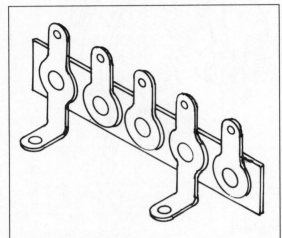

**Figure 2.5** *Typical section of tag strip. Various types are available, all are equally suitable for model railway use*

## Multi-pin plug & socket

The multi-pin plug and socket is an essential fitting for the portable layout. There are various types on the market, most of them fairly costly. Of late the 25-pin D type connector, primarily intended for computers and the like, has gained sway, largely because it is neat and probably the most cost-effective socket available.

The 2- 5- 7- and 9-pin DIN plugs and sockets, used mainly for audio circuits, are handy where only a few leads need to be connected.

Ex-equipment multi-pin connectors can often be picked up cheaply.

## Relays

The relay is a very useful device for model railway control. Fairly costly if bought new, one can often track down ex-equipment types. The PO 3000 type relay has a long history of service on model railways.

## Strowger switch

The strowger (or multi-selector) switch is a large rotary switch turned by an electro-magnet

*A multi-selector (Strowger) switch.*

*Two types of tag strip.*

*Screw pattern connectors in use.*

operating a ratchet. Originally invented to control automatic telephone switchboards, it has proved a useful adjunct to model railway automatic control. The only snag is that with the end of the old-pattern telephone exchange, it is disappearing from the ex-equipment market, and is somewhat costly when new.

Before I leave this subject, a word about tools. These are few in number and relatively inexpensive.

## Soldering iron

An electric soldering iron, together with paste flux and cored solder, is absolutely essential. For most work, the 15 watt instrument pattern is ideal, but a 25 watt iron is a useful reserve should you need to make a joint to a large piece of metal.

## Screwdrivers

A selection of small electrical screwdrivers will be needed, and could well be supplemented with a set of jeweller's screwdrivers, which are needed to get at the tiny screws one occasionally encounters in electrical devices.

## Pliers

You need at least one pair of pliers: fine snipe-nose are best. The bent nose type are frequently needed to insert wires into awkward places. A pair of heavy duty electrical-pattern snipe-nose pliers will be needed to tackle the heavier wires. Fine flat-nose pliers are needed should you have to adjust relay contacts.

## Wirecutters

Two pairs of wirecutters, a large general purpose type and a very small pair which can get into awkward corners, are best. With a limited budget, go for the heavy pair first.

## Wire strippers

Wire strippers are almost essential for removing plastic insulation from wires.

## Saw

A small six-inch pin-ended metal cutting saw is often needed to cut odd items.

## Drills

A set of twist drills, plus a suitable brace (or power drill) are essential. The larger types of switch require a 12mm hole, the sub-miniature fit into 7mm.

## Test meter

An inexpensive multi-meter and a set of test probes is an invaluable aid to trouble shooting. You do not require any great degree of accuracy, since there are few occasions on model railway electrification where you need to get within 2 V of the true reading. You will mostly be concerned with deciding between 6 and 12 V, or checking that there is 240 V ac on a certain pair of wires. The resistance range is the most useful, here you will only be concerned to see a full scale deflection, indicating that the circuit is properly made.

*Wire strippers.*

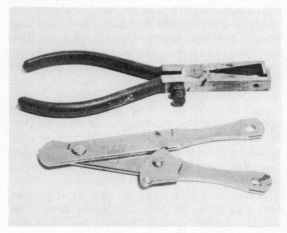

# CHAPTER 3

# Making joints

It is possible, just, to wire a model railway without using a soldering iron. It isn't a very good idea, for not only are crimped connections inferior, they are also more costly. So, before we do anything else, let's dispel the aura of mystery surrounding the technique of soft soldering.

Soldering was difficult in the bad old days, and I'm old enough to remember them. Before electric bits became readily available, it was necessary to take a massive lump of copper which was riveted to a heavy steel strap fitted into a large wooden handle, place it in the fire and, when it was hot enough, clean it, tin it and then make the joint before the copper cooled down. My father did his level best to teach me and, after many efforts, I did manage to make a proper joint. Then, having a few bob in my pocket, I cycled to every tool shop between the Isle of Dogs, where I was working at the time, and my home in Dagenham looking for an electric soldering iron. It was the summer of 1941, and everything was in short supply, but eventually I tracked one down. I never looked back.

Today, any DIY store worthy of the name can supply a 25 watt soldering iron with interchangeable bits. This is fine for our purposes, and will do a good many other jobs around the layout. A good model shop ought to be able to provide a 15 watt instrument bit, which is fine for electrification and usually has that invaluable fitting, a hook, although I prefer the soldering stand. Fit a 13 A flat pin plug, fused to 3 A, to the end of the lead, plug

in, switch on and we're in business.

Whilst the iron is getting up to its working temperature, let's go into the subject a little more deeply. Solder is an alloy of fusible metals, and is sold in various forms. For electrical wiring, cored solder, as sold in DIY stores and model shops, is the correct grade. Forget the rest.

Solder is not a glue, it has the property of linking with the metals it is joining. In other words, the solder does more than adhere to the base metal, it actually forms a molecular bond. It can only do this at the proper temperature, and this is where most beginners go wrong.

In addition, in order to make this bond, the surface of the base metal must be free from any oxide coating. This may be ensured by scraping, or rubbing with fine abrasive paper (wet and dry). The clean surface must be protected from further oxidation and, at the same time, the solder must be encouraged to flow freely over the surface. This is the function of the flux.

Having said all that, the majority of electrical joints don't call for that much preparation. Tags and terminals intended for soldered joints are normally provided with a tinned or plated finish and, unless you are using very old equipment, or parts that have had a lot of handling, they will take solder with only a minimum of flux. Likewise, freshly stripped electrical wire also takes solder easily, so the flux contained in the core of the solder is enough to do the job.

Let's therefore solder a wire to the tag of a panel-mounting toggle switch. First of all, we bare about 3mm of wire, using a wire stripper. This is then bent into a 'V' and hooked through the hole in the solder tag. This hooking is very important, for not only does it improve the mechanical strength of the joint, it holds the wire in position whilst you're applying the soldering iron and solder. People with three hands can, of course, ignore this. The wire is then squeezed together with fine-nosed pliers and the hot soldering iron is placed against the joint and then the cored solder is brought to the joint.

Assuming the iron is at working temperature, which will take about two minutes to achieve after switch-on, there will be a sharp fizz as the flux melts, then the solder will flow into a small bright blob. Remove the solder, then the iron (if you take the iron away first the stick of solder will, as often as not, weld itself to the joint), and leave the joint to harden.

The process is shown step by step in Fig 3.1; the result should be a small bright blob of solder covering the wire and flowing smoothly around the tag. When the solder has lost its bright mirror appearance, give the wire a gentle tug. If the joint has been properly made, it will stay there.

Earlier, I pointed out that it was essential to reach the working temperature. If the solder is not made hot enough you get a dry joint, which, instead of having negligible resistance, is a fairly good insulator. It is, fortunately, also a very weak joint, and almost invariably gives way at the first opportunity, which is why I told you to give the wire a tug.

When you gain experience, you will realize that solder at its working temperature has a bright, lively appearance, very much like mercury at room temperature. If it has a dull greyish tinge and moves sluggishly, you have not reached the right temperature and you will get a dry joint. With an electric iron this means you tried to solder too soon, or you didn't allow enough time for all parts to get hot enough. It will also happen all the time if you try to solder to a large lump of metal with a low-powered soldering

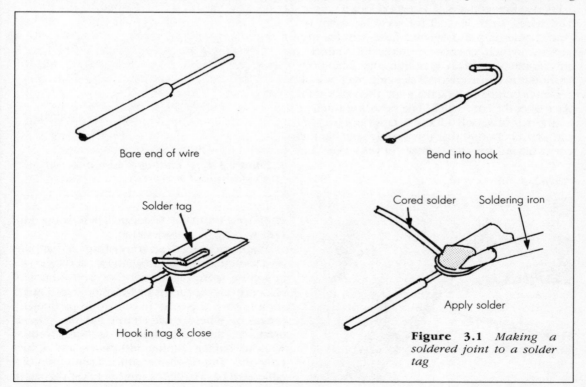

Bare end of wire

Bend into hook

Solder tag

Hook in tag & close

Cored solder     Soldering iron

Apply solder

**Figure 3.1** *Making a soldered joint to a solder tag*

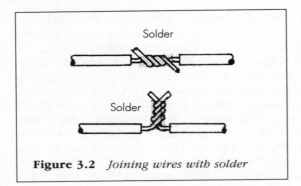

**Figure 3.2** *Joining wires with solder*

iron, but that is another story and is not likely to affect us at this stage.

Where it is necessary to join wires together, they should be twisted together and then soldered, as shown in Fig 3.2. The in-line method is neater, and rather easier to insulate, but in practice it is simpler to twist the wires at right angles and then solder. The T-shaped projection may then be bent flat before insulating.

Even at low voltages, it is a good idea to cover bare wires, since it is all too easy for them to touch something and create a false path for the current, which creates unpredictable effects, only some of which are amusing. The best method is to slip a length of sleeving over one of the wires before making the joint, then slide it in place over the bare wires. The next best thing is to wrap a little self-adhesive tape around the joint, remembering that this is only suitable for low voltage use and must never, ever be

*Making a joint to a tag strip.*

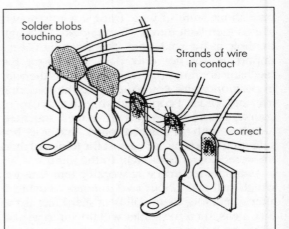

**Figure 3.3** *Badly made joints on a tag strip leading to short circuits and false paths*

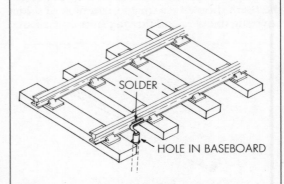

**Figure 3.4** *Soldering a wire to a rail to provide a feed or return*

employed on mains voltages. There is no third best worthy of consideration.

When soldering to an array of tags, as happens on a switch, or on tag strip, the great danger lies in getting spare bits of wire, or even lumps of solder, bridging the space between tags. Fig 3.3 shows how this can occur; it is particularly prevalent where multi-strand flexible wire is used, or where equipment is being reused without having all the old wires and solder removed. The results are, once again, unpredictable, so it pays to check carefully. A small pair of wire cutters should be wielded with care to clean up the space between tags.

Soldering to a prepared tag is not too difficult, but soldering a wire to a rail calls for just a little more trouble, since it is probable that the rail itself isn't very clean. You must scrape the tarnish away first, and to do this I generally use a small electrician's screwdriver, which fits into the groove of the rail as if it were made for the task. I also prefer to add a dab of flux. Fig 3.4 shows how one carries the wire down through a hole in the baseboard, and how the business end of the wire is bent to fit snugly into the web of the rail. If this is done carefully, it is not really as unsightly as might appear from the drawing, but where finescale standards are employed, it is worth taking the trouble to hide the wire completely. One method is to solder a bare dropper wire to one of the fixings before laying the rail, and then to connect the main wire to the dropper. Of course this involves extra work and a high degree of pre-planning, but this is implicit in finescale modelling.

Nowadays I prefer to use phosphoric acid flux on track; it is less messy than the older, but very reliable paste flux. You can buy phosphoric acid flux under various trade names, or you can get a supply of Jenolite rust clearing fluid and dilute it half-and-half with tap water. Yes, I know that you are supposed to use de-ionized water, on the grounds that tap water has odd things in it, dissolved lime salts and the like. Well, all I can say is that you'd be hard put to find harder water than the stuff that comes out of my taps, and my 50-50 mixture works a treat. I'm also told that it rots metals unless thoroughly washed off, but, after over a decade of use, I'm still waiting for this to happen.

The main thing to watch when soldering a wire to plastic based track is to do it quickly before you melt the fixings. You need, therefore, to use a hot iron, and keep it in contact with the rail for no more than a couple of seconds. If you feel at all unsure of yourself, solder to a rail joiner. This is why Peco advise against soldering, but a maker of plastic based track is clearly not going to advise a practice that, in careless hands, can lead to damage. However, I've soldered hundreds of joints on Peco

Streamline without the slightest trouble, but for all that I'd advise newcomers to the craft to practise beforehand and not to solder to the more expensive turnouts, except under dire need. Having said that, I have soldered wires to Peco points without damaging them.

In point of fact, soldering is a remarkably quick technique once you've got over your initial hesitant moves. Furthermore, it is the method that offers the least electrical resistance per square millimetre of joint area.

There are two other types of electrical joint you will encounter. One is the screw socket, the type largely used for 240 V supplies. You'll find it on some types of equipment, a number of miniature plugs and, most commonly of all, in the common screw terminal strip. You can get these, on cards, in DIY stores at about a 50 per cent premium over the price of loose versions in a proper electrician's. Best of all, there are many firms who have even cheaper lots in boxes on their stands at model railway exhibitions. This is where I get mine. This, incidentally, is the one piece of equipment you can buy at bargain prices in the confident knowledge that it must be OK.

The use of screw terminal strips is self evident – or is it? There are a couple of small details to consider. First of all, if you're using the strip as a splitting junction, in other words, you're fanning a number of wires out of one socket, you need the larger patterns simply to take all the wires. However, if you find that there are just one or two in the strip that need a number of leads, you can double up, linking an adjacent pair together with a small wire link.

Where multistrand flexible cable is being used, it is essential to twist the strands closely together before securing them in a pinch socket. If you're very meticulous, it's even better to solder the end of the flex before making the joint. It is not a good idea to twist several single core wires together if your joint socket is at all small, it only tends to make the overall size of the wire larger than it need be.

The other type of socket is the screw-down pattern. There is one simple rule with this type of terminal, always wrap the wire around the screw so that, as you tighten the nut, you tend to

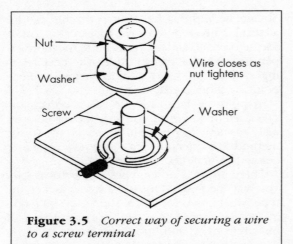

**Figure 3.5** *Correct way of securing a wire to a screw terminal*

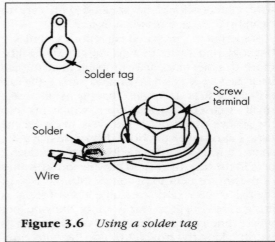

**Figure 3.6** *Using a solder tag*

tighten the wire around the post. This is shown in Fig 3.5. With single core wire, you form the loop either around a small rod – often the shank of the ubiquitous small screwdriver – or with a pair of round-nose pliers. With flex you have, I find, three options. The first is to solder the end of the wire, converting it into a single unit, whereupon it can be treated as single core. The second, the one I generally favour, is to make a complete loop by winding the flex around the

rod and then twisting the end around to form a complete loop. Once again, a quick wipe with a hot soldering iron improves matters.

A third method, which is strongly recommended for permanent connection, is to slip a solder tag under the screw terminal and solder the wire directly to this. Fig 3.6 shows the arrangement, but I should stress that *this is not suited to anything other than low voltage circuits*, since it exposes far too much bare metal.

# CHAPTER 4
# Points and crossings

I mentioned earlier that it is essential to keep feed and return apart. This is easy enough until one comes to a pair of points or a diamond crossing, and since a model railway without points is nothing more than a toy train set dressed up beyond its station, we have to do something about it.

The simplest solution is to use a dead frog. I'm not suggesting that you kill an innocent amphibian; the device we're discussing is more correctly termed an insulated crossing, but as is so often the case, we have a different term within the hobby. In essence, instead of a metal crossing, which permanently connects both rails elec-

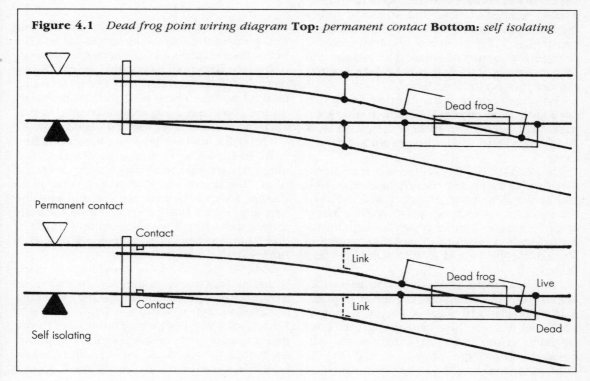

**Figure 4.1**  *Dead frog point wiring diagram* **Top:** *permanent contact* **Bottom:** *self isolating*

Dead frog

Permanent contact

Contact

Link

Dead frog

Live

Contact

Link

Dead

Self isolating

trically, we use one made from an insulating material, generally plastic. The rails are bonded across underneath and the current is carried across without any bother. This arrangement is shown in the upper section of Fig 4.1. It is simple in application, but has its limitations.

Unfortunately, the train isn't always carried across so easily as the electricity, for the elementary dead frog forms a rather large gap in the conductive path and, as a result, the train tends to jerk or even stop as it goes over the frog. In extreme cases, it stops altogether. Commercial points avoid this by very sophisticated designs which, unfortunately are not easily copied in the home workshop, and hence the dead frog is primarily found on commercial turnouts.

I am confining my remarks to three makes, Hornby, Peco and Fleischmann, since these are the types I have had most experience with. Each offer, in addition to the dead frog, automatic isolation of sidings and loops. This is done by switching the current to the point blade so that the rail not in contact with the stock rail is electrically isolated, unless fed in some other fashion. The arrangement is shown in the lower part of Fig 4.1. This is extremely convenient, as it saves providing special isolation for sidings, and so locomotives or trains can be held there whilst another runs on the main line.

The Hornby point is the most elementary. It has a fairly large insulated section, and no great pains have been taken to hide the pivots. It is fairly rugged and will withstand a good deal of abuse.

The Peco INSULFROG point is more refined: the pivots of the point blades are hidden, and it is within the limitations of price, and the constraints of the rail section, a good, realistic model of the prototype. Careful design has kept the insulated section down to the absolute minimum needed to cope with wider than standard wheel flanges.

The Fleischmann point does not disguise its blade pivots, but otherwise, like the Peco point, is a very good model of the prototype. It has two additional features: first, two spring wire links are fitted in the factory, cutting out the self-isolation. These are shown dotted in the diagram. At the same time, the point blades are

so free that all but the very lightest of rolling stock can push them over. It is therefore possible to use these points as uncontrolled spring points at loops, aiding automatic and semi-automatic operation of a layout.

It is possible to remove the toggle spring from a Peco point, and make it perform in the same fashion, but the point blades will need to be hard wired to the stock rails to remove the automatic isolation. This is best done by linking the rails beyond the point, rather than soldering to the point itself, which would void the makers' generous warranty. Alternatively, a small spring contact can be forced between the rails, as in the Fleischmann pattern.

The main advantage of the dead frog point is that, in theory, no special attention need be paid when the layout is being wired, since there is no way you can make feed meet return. However, to get the best from the self-isolating pattern, we should observe:

## RULE 4    Always feed current to the toe end of a point.

Fig 4.2 shows this in action. We have the one feed point at the start of the simple ladder. The heavy lines indicate rails connected to the controller, the light ones rails which are electrically dead. It will be seen that only the route set up receives power to both rails, and therefore only on this route will a locomotive be able to run; anything in the sidings will be isolated.

This is fine until we introduce some complications. In Fig 4.3 we have a series of sidings fanning off a separate road which forms a convenient shunting neck. With the points set as shown, all appears well, we can run into the shunting neck. However, as Fig 4.4 clearly shows, the moment we try to shunt a wagon or coach into a siding our shunting neck is dead. A further dotted feed is needed.

So far, so good, but as we could shunt the yard whilst another train is running on the main line, it could be more convenient to feed the shunting neck from another controller. This is shown in Fig 4.5. All will go swimmingly until you throw the crossover with both controllers switched on. Putting two controllers into parallel like this produces some interesting results, but it doesn't

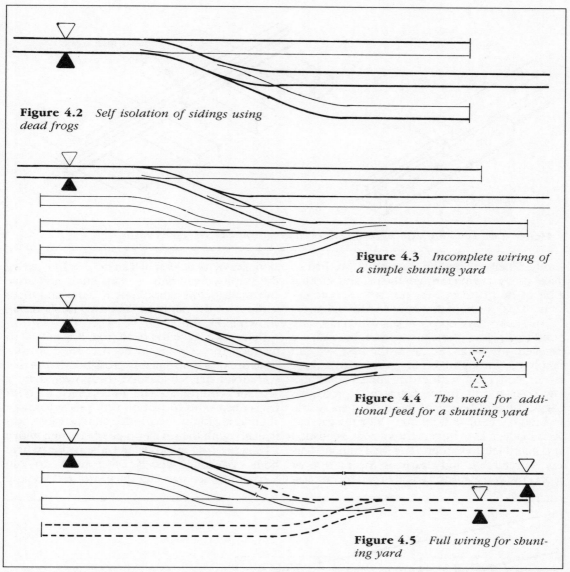

**Figure 4.2** *Self isolation of sidings using dead frogs*

**Figure 4.3** *Incomplete wiring of a simple shunting yard*

**Figure 4.4** *The need for additional feed for a shunting yard*

**Figure 4.5** *Full wiring for shunting yard*

always make the locomotive move in any direction, let alone the one we want. If we put rail breaks between the two points forming the crossover, then the controllers cannot be cross-connected; thus we get:

**RULE 5** Always have double rail-breaks where points are back to back, as at a crossover.

I have been talking glibly of rail-breaks; it is now essential to look more closely at the subject. The idea is to insulate two lengths of rail from each other so that either one side is isolated (dead), or the sections on either side of a rail break are fed by different controllers. Today, we have insulating fishplates made from plastic and provided, in the centre, with a small plastic nub which prevents the rails being pushed up against one

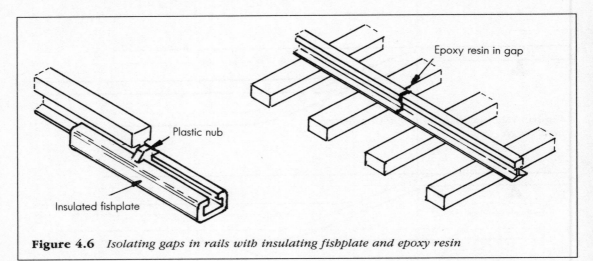

**Figure 4.6** *Isolating gaps in rails with insulating fishplate and epoxy resin*

another. Before they were available, we had to make do by sawing through the rail and sticking a bit of thin card in between with acetate cement. This, we hoped, would remain in place.

Today, we have epoxy resins which not only bond two pieces of metal together, but also are excellent insulators. So, as in the past, we can simply cut through the rail, either with a razor saw or, better still, with a small abrasive disc on a low voltage drill. In the latter case, protective goggles should be worn; those discs are brittle and can break up and fly out. Once the gap has been made, a little mixed epoxy resin is pushed into it and left to harden. The 'five minute' variety is preferable, and clearly, in the interests of economy, you insulate a batch of gaps in one ses-

sion. Leave for at least half an hour before paring the surplus away with a sharp knife, and leave overnight before smoothing the top and inner surfaces of the rail head. The two methods are shown in Fig 4.6.

Before we leave the dead frog, it is as well to mention the crossing in Fig 4.7. Here all four frogs are dead and suitably cross-bonded so that each road may, if desired, be powered by a separate controller. The multiplicity of dead frogs makes this formation very prone to cause shuddering of the loco; indeed it is possible, particularly with the smaller type of crossing with a 24 degree frog angle, to get a situation where both collecting wheels of a ready to run locomotive are standing on an isolated section.

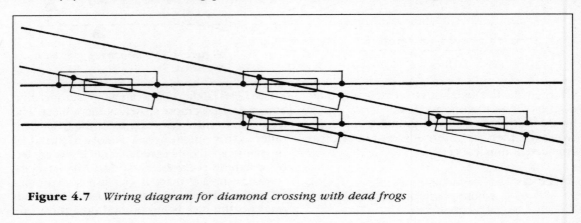

**Figure 4.7** *Wiring diagram for diamond crossing with dead frogs*

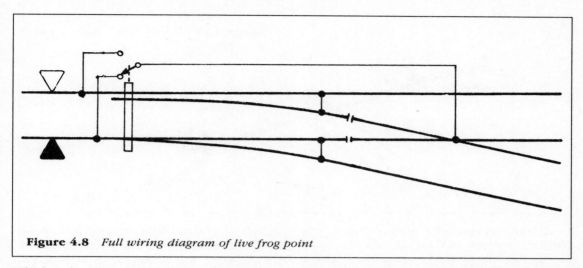

**Figure 4.8**  *Full wiring diagram of live frog point*

Which isn't quite what we want! This is where live frogs become necessary.

As I said earlier, it is virtually impossible to make an effective dead frog point in the home workshop. Apart from that, the live frog point is technically superior, though it is rather more involved, electrically. Furthermore, unlike the dead frog turnout, which can be used after a fashion even if Rules 4 and 5 are broken, where live frogs are concerned, failure to observe these rules means that, sooner rather than later, Rule 3 is also broken, and the cut-out in the controller shuts off power. One hopes!

It is, in theory, perfectly possible to make a live frog point with no internal breaks, and to rely on the contact between the point blades,

aided by some form of simple sliding contact, to change the polarity of the frog. However, the weakness with point blade contact is its essential unreliability, and so the preferred method of wiring a two-rail turnout is shown in Fig 4.8, using a changeover switch coupled to the tiebar to energize the frog. It is also advisable to isolate the frog from the point blades, and to bond these to the adjacent stockrail, so that you do not get both feed and return a matter of a few millimetres apart – until a wheel passes through, whereupon the gap comes down to less than a millimetre and, on occasions, disappears altogether.

In Fig 4.9 I have eliminated the connecting wires and use, instead, code letters and numbers

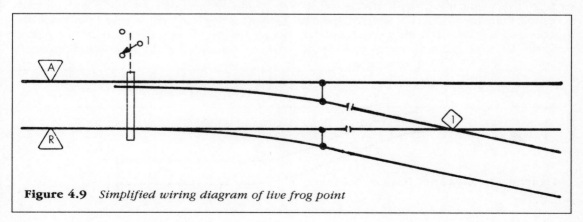

**Figure 4.9**  *Simplified wiring diagram of live frog point*

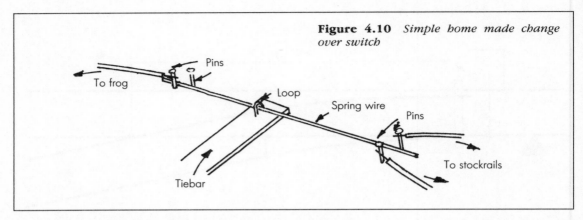

**Figure 4.10** *Simple home made change over switch*

Pins

To frog

Loop

Spring wire

Pins

To stockrails

Tiebar

for each connection to the track or switch. This detached contact method of describing the wiring of a control circuit is a great deal easier to follow, since you do not have to trace long and involved nets of lines on the diagram; instead, you locate the two positions that need to be joined. Which is, of course, what you actually do when you start the practical side of wiring.

This arrangement requires a separate change-over switch, which can be a relatively simple affair. Fig 4.10 shows one popular system, a piece of springy wire fixed at one end to the baseboard, and in its middle to the point blade. Two pins, connected to the rails as shown, are placed a couple of millimetres apart and wires are taken from these pins to the running rails. The fixed end of the spring wire is wired to the frog. This very elementary changeover switch works well because the spring wire rubs against each pin every time it is thrown. It's also nicely accessible for maintenance, but nevertheless it is a good idea to cover it with a small wooden walkway, to protect it and to keep most of the

dust off of it. A much better arrangement is to use a microswitch to change the polarity of the frog. This can be fitted either at the point itself or, if controls and turnouts are reasonably close together, to the leverframe.

With this arrangement, one gets siding isolation, exactly as with an isolating dead frog turnout, though in this case, instead of the dead road having one rail isolated, both rails are connected either to feed or to return, as shown in Fig 4.11. This seems odd at first sight, since we are used to thinking it essential to have at least one wire to a device broken by means of a switch to prevent it operating. It is just as effective to connect both terminals, or in the case of a locomotive, both pick-ups to one output, since the device is then shorted out.

It is as well to pause and look at how we arrange points in an actual layout. Fig 4.12 shows the common or garden oval track, with turnouts feeding sidings, a trifle toylike, but none the worse for that. If we are using dead frog points, then we can simply push the connecting plug in

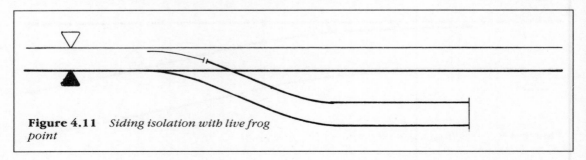

**Figure 4.11** *Siding isolation with live frog point*

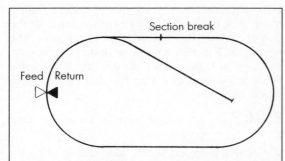

**Figure 4.12** *Wiring an oval track with live frog point*

front of all point toes and go from there. If we are using live frogs, then the double rail-break at position X is essential, if we are not to set up a short circuit every time we throw a point to a siding, breaking Rule 3 in the process! So we have:

**RULE 6**    There should always be a double break on any continuous run.

I should at this juncture mention that, if there is only one point involved, or all points are either inside or outside the oval, then you can get away with one rail break. The trouble is that the rules that tell you which rail you break are rather complicated, and so, many years ago, I realized that putting a double break solved a lot of problems, as well as taking care of future extensions.

There is an interesting consequence of this arrangement. What happens when, on the continuous circuit, a locomotive approaches a point from behind, which is set against it? Doesn't it bridge the gap and link feed with return? In

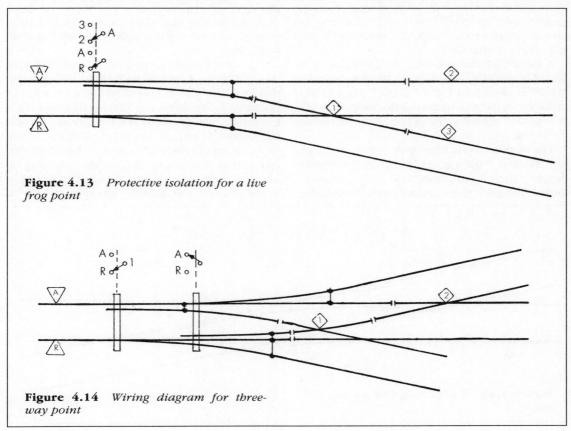

**Figure 4.13** *Protective isolation for a live frog point*

**Figure 4.14** *Wiring diagram for three-way point*

theory, yes; in practice, as often as not, no; it skids across and stops with all collecting wheels on the far side. Either way, the train stops before it runs into the point and derails, which is a good thing.

There is, however, a more elegant approach, which I show in Fig 4.13. Here there are two isolating sections, at least one loco long, fed from a further changeover switch linked to the tiebar. When the point is set against a road, the isolating section is dead and so the loco stops on a proper isolating section. This arrangement can be provided on any type of point, but as it adds another changeover switch and more complications, it should be reserved for locations where there is a reasonable probability that an operator may be driving his train along merrily, quite unaware that he is approaching a point, let alone that it is set against him. It makes sense at junctions and also at the ends of platforms, and, as a general rule, need only be included where, on the prototype (and, I trust, the model) there is a stop signal alongside.

A three-way point is only a little more complicated, since so long as you stagger the point blades as shown in Fig 4.14, not only will you make the wiring quite straightforward, but you will greatly simplify the actual construction of the point.

The double slip is best dealt with by connecting all four blades at each end to a common tiebar. Once again, this not only simplifies wiring, but also makes the mechanical construc-

tion much easier. The two independent tiebars mean that the four possible routes through the unit are set by the operation of two levers. The wiring, as Fig 4.15 shows, is quite simple, providing you realize that a double slip is the same thing as two points toe to toe, but takes up less space. Hence:

**RULE 7**  A double slip is always a feed point.

We now return to the live frog diamond crossing. This is generally considered to be something of a beast, since we have four frogs, each of which has to swap feeds, not merely with normal feed and return, but generally with two separate sets of feeds from the up and down controller. Some horrendously complex wiring diagrams have been published, all of which involve a switch on the panel that must be manually selected. Hence many people adopt dead frogs as the only sane alternative, which does at least avoid one getting mixed up with special switchgear.

This never made sense to me, but the more I thought about it, the more it came home to me that the error was in considering the crossing in isolation. Apart from the toylike figure-of-eight formation, which I think we can ignore, a crossing always forms part of a point complex. If one looks along the track for a little, it becomes obvious that the route across the crossing is selected by another point. The simplest example is, of course, the double junction, which is

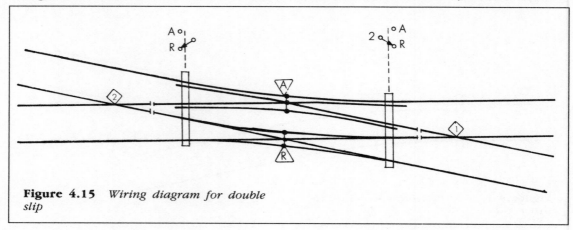

**Figure 4.15** *Wiring diagram for double slip*

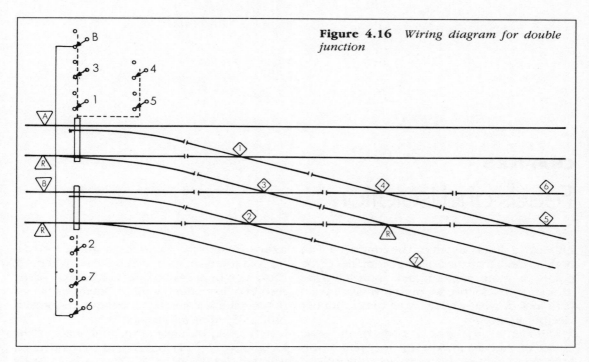

**Figure 4.16** *Wiring diagram for double junction*

shown in Fig 4.16. The wiring gets quite involved, since we have not only four possible combinations, but two isolating sections on top of the six frogs, two for the points and four for the diamond.

You will see that one point, the controlling point, has four changeover switches, whilst the other has two. There are two isolating sections which are quite optional and exist merely to prevent you driving a train through the roads that are set against it. Why are these isolating sections provided in only one pair of roads? Well, I'm assuming that you are going to use your double track in a prototypical fashion and run on the left. As a result, you will not be driving towards the other point, so it doesn't need protecting! Of course, if you run wrong road there could be trouble, but that too is prototypical.

I have touched only lightly on protective isolation, since, in the next chapter I shall be considering this along with the whole question of feeds and isolation.

# CHAPTER 5
# Feeds and isolation

Although a simple layout can be controlled with nothing more than the isolating properties of the points, a more sophisticated approach pays dividends. To do this, we must first take a good hard look at what we are trying to do with our electrification.

Although a great deal is made of the scale aspect of model railways, in my opinion this only serves to mask the true object, the realistic simulation of a full-sized operating system. The object of electrification is to enable us to work our lines realistically. Given prototypically correct track plans, this can be done with nothing more elaborate than wire and switches, backed up in certain cases with relays. It is as well to stress that 'prototypically correct' does not mean a slavish copy of an actual prototype, rather a layout based on full-sized practice.

The basic rule of railway operation is that, under normal circumstances, only one train is allowed to move in any one section at any one time. We must, of course, remember that in this context 'train' can include a single locomotive, as well as railcars, multiple units and anything else that is capable of moving under its own power on the track.

On the home layout, another consideration makes it advisable for only one locomotive to be moving at once, the fact that the owner/ builder/operator can only easily control one locomotive at a time, and certainly, is only able to follow the movement of one locomotive closely. There are ways of getting two loco-motives to move at once without asking for trouble, but these are governed by very rigid rules, backed up by specialized sectionalization of the section of layout in question. Otherwise, whilst the operator is attending to one train, the other is probably getting into trouble.

As a result, for most of the time, most of the locomotives on a layout should be standing on isolating sections of track. This can be done by putting them in sidings and setting the points against them, but the provision of additional isolating sections aids operation out of all recognition. But before we go any further, we must familiarize ourselves with the wiring symbols I have been using for some forty years to show where the various feeds, rail breaks and isolating sections are situated on the layout.

These are shown in Fig 5.1. We have already met the feed and return symbols, and, by implication, the double rail-break used to isolate one section from another. The new one is the small loop which denotes the isolating section.

**Figure 5.1**   *Symbols for feeds and breaks*

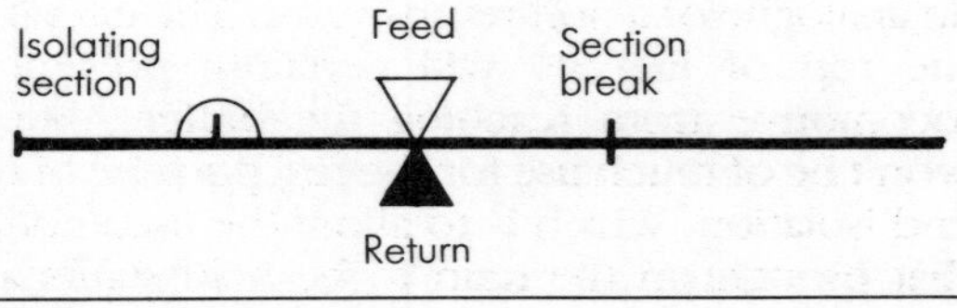

Isolating section | Feed | Section break

Return

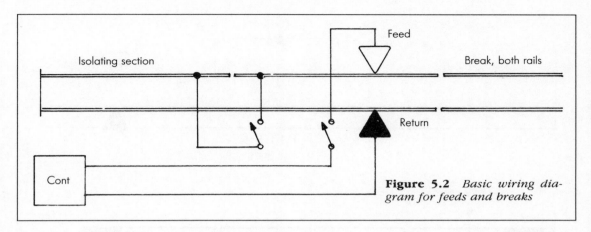

**Figure 5.2** *Basic wiring diagram for feeds and breaks*

To help clarify the position, Fig 5.2 shows the basic wiring diagram. All returns go directly to the controller, and the feed is connected through a switch; in the simple arrangement shown, this is an on/off or SPST type.

An isolating section is usually found on a dead-end of track. It consists of an insulated gap, generally in the feed rail, but it can equally be in the return. An on/off switch is wired across the gap to provide continuity.

Isolating sections are generally provided at the ends of terminal roads, and frequently their purpose is completely misunderstood. They are not provided to prevent one running a train into the buffers, any more than one would place several redundant mattresses at the end of one's garage to take care of the odd collision. Instead the train should be driven properly and brought slowly to a stop with the locomotive bufferbeam around 10mm from the end and, much more to the purpose, with the rear auto coupling just beyond the uncoupling ramp, ready to allow the engine to be detached from the train.

The idea that the isolating section was a protective device has led to many writers proposing that the section is fed through a diode, which is an electronic device that, with dc current, acts as an analogue of a non-return valve. The circuit at the top of Fig 5.3 will certainly prevent a locomotive from reaching the buffers, but it won't be of much use for the real purpose of the end isolation, which is to allow the locomotive that brought in the train to be held stationary

whilst another is put on the other end to take the train out again. This is shown in the lower part of Fig 5.3, which demonstrates that the diode arrangement would not work, since as you drive the train out, the first locomotive simply follows its tail. If you want to prevent an accidental collision with the buffers, replace the on/off switch with a push-button, or, more simply, leave the switch in the off position.

As we have seen, the purpose of an isolating section is to allow us to prevent a locomotive from moving, even if the road on which it is standing is energized. This applies in considerable force in a locomotive depot, where you have room to stable several locomotives along one length of track. Here the switches are wired across successive gaps, to prevent the far end being energized whilst the nearer sections are still dead and, presumably, have locomotives standing on them. This is shown in Fig 5.4 which depicts what, on the prototype, would be a very modest MPD, but is about as large as can be accommodated on the average layout. It provides standing for six locomotives in the two shed roads, with provision to hold three in the valeting roads leading to and from the turntable. The far siding, shown as standing for the breakdown train, is sub-divided into four, on the basic premise that you usually discover that you need additional standing as the layout develops and it is easier to provide for it at the outset. No isolation is provided on the road to the coaling stage, since, although a shunting tank might be

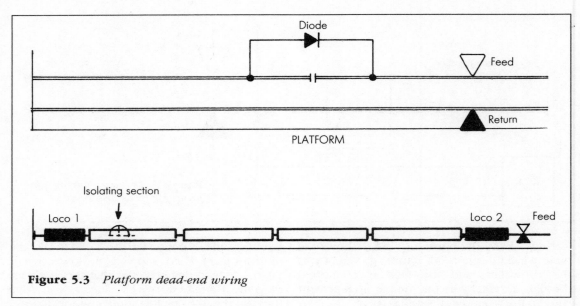

**Figure 5.3** *Platform dead-end wiring*

held here temporarily, this can be handled by the self-isolation provided through the point.

Before I leave the locomotive depot, I will deal with the wiring of the turntable. A lot will depend on whether it is a ready-built unit, in which case the instructions supplied should include the necessary wiring diagram, or whether it is scratchbuilt, or made from a plastic kit. In the latter cases, you have to get current to the tracks yourself.

It is no use attaching wires to the rails, you will only tie things in a knot. Worse, when the turntable has been reversed, which is of course its primary purpose, the rails will be connected the wrong way round. It is ridiculously simple to avoid all this trouble.

All prototype turntables are supported at their

ends on a circular rail. On the model, this is purely cosmetic, since we can provide a simple rigid bearing in the centre. However, by splitting the rail into two halves and providing collectors at each end of the table as shown in Fig 5.5, we not only are able to pick up current and turn the table, but as soon as it has gone half-way round, the relative polarities of the deck rails are automatically reversed.

It is not absolutely essential to provide separate isolation for the turntable feed, unless you want to shunt the locomotive depot whilst a locomotive is being turned. As this would only happen with a motorized table, it is generally best to provide for this in the control wiring, which I do not propose to consider. Motorized turntables soon become fiendishly complicated

**Figure 5.4** *Isolating sections in a motive power depot*

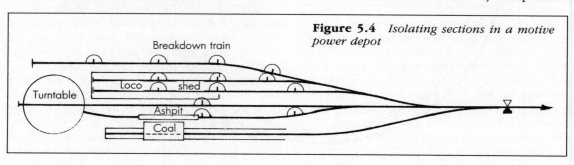

and the basic rule is, if you can't work out the wiring, don't attempt to build it, but stick instead to a simple manual worm-and-wheel drive. By the same token, using the turntable to energize the road selected is also best avoided, other than on roundhouse-pattern sheds, and once again, if you don't know how to arrange it, stick to the simple system of isolating each shed road manually.

It is advisable to provide isolation on all sidings and loops where locomotives are held, as a matter of course since, although a point can provide isolation, you might accidentally throw it and have the locomotive start when you don't wish it, or, worse, if the point contact is faulty, a false path can be made through the locomotive motor windings with the result that, as the main line locomotive approaches, the 'dead' locomotive in the siding begins to move forward.

The usual result is a collision at the point, the more annoying because there is little one can do to prevent it, other than shutting off power and manhandling the stock.

There is a further consideration, that the switch on the panel can provide a reminder that a locomotive occupies the section. There are two simple methods, the first is to keep isolating switches normally on, only putting them off when a locomotive is held there. A more positive arrangement, invaluable in a locomotive depot, is to provide small tokens to hang on the switch toggle, as in Fig 5.6. This is an analogue of the collar provided in manual signal boxes to remind a signalman that a train is standing by the relevant signal, and while it is difficult to provide the positive stop of the collar, this arrangement works quite well in the model world.

It is worthwhile, at this part of the pro-

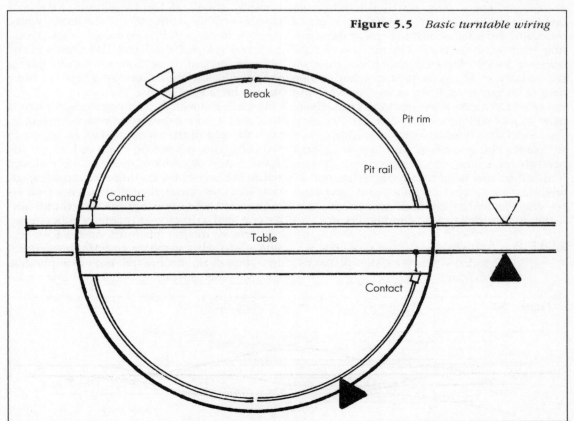

**Figure 5.5**  *Basic turntable wiring*

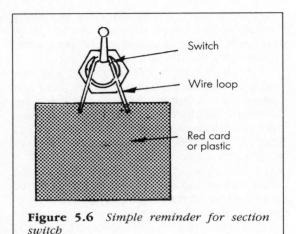

**Figure 5.6** *Simple reminder for section switch*

ceedings, to emphasize that in full-sized railways, elaborate interlocking is essential for a number of reasons. For a start, up to a hundred individuals can be concerned with the passage of one train, and it is essential to prevent them getting their wires crossed. On the model, one operator does the lot. Next, a simple collision on the prototype usually at least means that one item of rolling stock is the worse for wear and has to be taken out of service. Models take quite hard knocks with little or no damage. Finally, if the model train does have any passengers, they are plastic and cannot be hurt. So we do not need to ape every aspect of prototype protection, we merely need to be able to use our intelligence to prevent collisions and runaways. So, very elementary methods are perfectly adequate. In fact they can be summed up in:

**RULE 8**    An isolating section should be provided wherever a locomotive has to stand.

As a stop signal is a place where a locomotive will frequently stop, it is advisable to use signals to show where isolating breaks should occur. A section can be linked to a stop signal, utilizing a contact on the operating relay. If the signal is worked other than by a small relay, then a double pole switch will be needed at the control panel, and a lot more wire. With this arrangement, a locomotive cannot pass a stop signal; a slight improvement on the prototype.

In any case, as we frequently need to hold locomotives alongside signals we get:

**RULE 9**    It must always be possible to isolate a train positively against a stop signal.

Whilst the interaction of signals and sections is a fascinating subject, it will be the subject of a later book by myself, and so I shall turn to the consideration of the wiring of typical station layouts, a simple through station on a single track layout. You will see in Fig 5.7 that I've drawn in the main features of the station, since these have a very significant bearing on just where we place the rail breaks and feeds.

Dealing first with the running roads, we have a feed at each end of the station which will link up with the rest of the layout and allow us to run trains through the station. We need to provide some means of holding trains in the platform roads; this is essential if a single track passing station is to be operated prototypically. Two arrangements are shown. Approaching the up platform, a feed is provided to energize either the up platform or the bay platform. An isolating section is provided at the up end of this platform, fed through the final point, and corresponding roughly with the starting signal, enabling a train

**Figure 5.7** *Feeds and breaks for a single-track passing station*

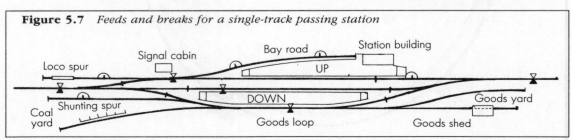

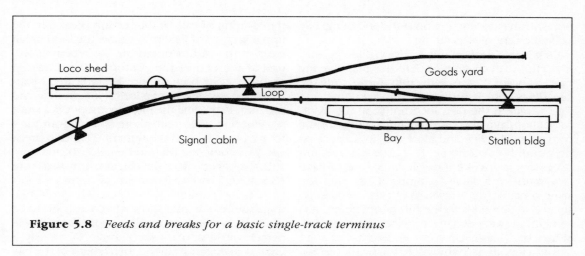

**Figure 5.8** *Feeds and breaks for a basic single-track terminus*

Labels within figure: Loco shed, Loop, Signal cabin, Goods yard, Bay, Station bldg

to be held here whilst it is waiting for the section ahead to clear. The whole of the down platform forms a complete section; once again, a complete train can be isolated with a switch on the panel. Both arrangements work equally well, but the former is capable of more sophistication, since not only is the isolating section closely associated with the starting signal, but it is possible to allow a train to run into this road without a hand on the controller, knowing it will come to a halt safely. This allows one operator to bring two trains into the station simultaneously, without any need for a computer-controlled controller and elaborate electronic devices in the locomotives. An on/off switch, carefully located, can often do the work of a bevy of microprocessors! Furthermore, with command control (see Appendix 4) one really needs two operators to perform this trick.

The bay platform has the usual isolating section at its end, but has an additional isolating section at the end of the platform. With this, a train can be standing in the bay, ready to depart and another locomotive brought into the road. This would allow one to double head the train; indeed, the extra isolation provided at each platform road permits one to attach a pilot locomotive to the head of the train. Once again, this is the sort of manoeuvre that is associated with command control. The locomotive spur, which is also isolated, is needed if you intend to reverse non push-pull locomotive hauled trains in the

bay, but is mainly there for the station pilot.

The goods loop has its own feed and as a result, except when it is necessary to run round stock, shunting can take place whilst a busy service is run on the main line. However, as there are sidings at each end of the loop, you will need to run round occasionally. A further isolating section is provided at the far end of the shunting spur, another spot to hold a locomotive.

Many of these isolating sections appear redundant, in the sense that they are not needed to electrify the line, nor are they absolutely essential for basic operation. However, they do provide the opportunity to carry out much more complex movements involving two locomotives, without the need for complex, costly devices and special fittings in every locomotive.

We now turn in Fig 5.8 to the simple branch terminus. This elementary plan is going to crop up several times throughout the book, since its basic nature makes it an ideal subject when we come to consider control panels and point control. It also on this occasion demonstrates the importance of locating section breaks correctly in relation to the main features of the station itself.

The wiring is very simple, three feeds and two isolating sections. In practice, you won't need any more than this on so basic a station, where it is very unusual for there to be two locomotives in the station at once. So why bother to have any switched feeds, why not link the feeds as well as the returns, and leave it at that? The point isolation and an isolating section at the end of the bay will take care of everything.

Or will it? The terminus at Seaton, Devon, was, if anything, even simpler than this plan, having one less point. Yet from the mid-thirties until the late fifties, on Saturdays in season, you could find a train in the bay, locomotive at the front, full of holidaymakers waiting impatiently for the next train to arrive and clear the single track so they could set off home. It is clear that it is un-necessary to invoke modeller's licence to have two trains in a small terminus at one and the same time. As the presence of two trains in so small a station adds to the fun of operation, it is something we need to be able to carry out. When this happens, you need to be able to isolate a locomotive anywhere on the model. So, every feed has to be switchable if you are to get the most out of the layout. This brings us to:

**RULE 10**  It should be possible to isolate every section of track, even though the controller is fully energized.

Before we leave this station, we need to consider the location of two of the section breaks. In the upper section of Fig 5.9 we have the loop break clear of the platform and the bay isolating sec-tion at the end of the platform. I've drawn in trains to show how the breaks (indicated by ar-rows) are situated in relation to locomotive and coaches. Providing the bay locomotive is a small six-wheeled tank, then there is just room for a four-wheeled van at the buffers. The loop break allows a complete train to be held isolated.

In the lower part of the diagram, the breaks are relocated. The bay isolator now allows a short train to be completely isolated. This could be quite useful; it would allow a two-car DMU to be isolated, or there would be room for a bogie parcels van clear of the locomotive. Obviously, a great deal depends on the total length of the bay road, but I think I have shown how careful posi-tioning increases the operating potential.

At the same time, moving the loop section break back allows a second locomotive to be backed on to the train. This might seem pur-poseless on so small a layout; it certainly stret-ches credulity beyond all reasonable limits and calls for a suspension of a modeller's licence. However, were the same basic layout length-

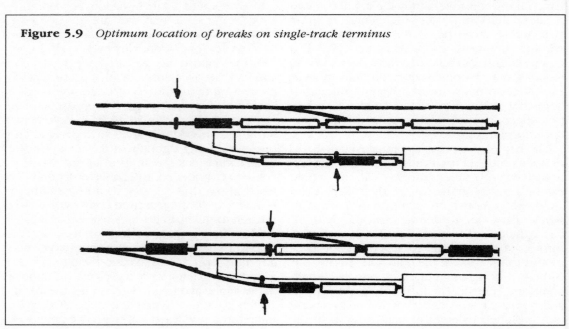

**Figure 5.9**  *Optimum location of breaks on single-track terminus*

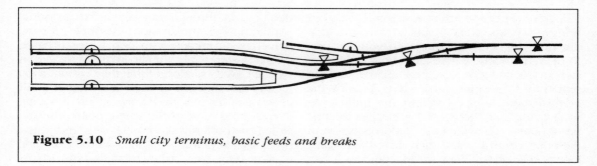

**Figure 5.10** *Small city terminus, basic feeds and breaks*

ened, and provided not only with additional sidings, but a turntable as well as a locomotive shed, suggesting it served a resort the size of Newquay or Ilfracombe, then exchanging tender locomotives in this fashion would be acceptable.

I show in Fig 5.10 my most popular plan, Minories, a three-platform city terminus with just six points. The basic sectionalizing is shown; this is perfectly workable, and capable of fairly extensive operation.

However, Minories was designed for suburban tank locomotives. There is no easy way of turning tender locomotives, and in city stations,

tender-first working is highly improbable. It is ideally suited to intensive diesel-era operation, since diesels don't need to be turned. Furthermore, let us take things to their logical conclusion and make the platforms long enough to hold a complete seven-coach HST. We now have a model which, at exhibitions, offers the opportunity of running a wide variety of present-day trains, and is a certain attraction.

There is just one point to remember, a platform that can take a true-length HST will also accommodate two DMU sets. So, in Fig 5.11 I have provided some extra section breaks, and given each platform an independent feed.

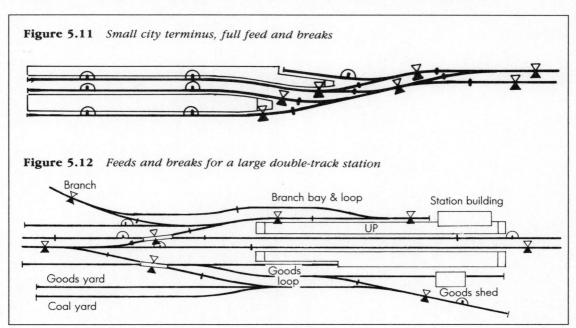

**Figure 5.11** *Small city terminus, full feed and breaks*

**Figure 5.12** *Feeds and breaks for a large double-track station*

Branch

Branch bay & loop

Station building

UP

Goods yard

Goods loop

Goods shed

Coal yard

Two new features are now possible. You can bring in a six-coach DMU, split it in two and send out two independent trains, and you can perform this manoeuvre in reverse. Better still, with cab control and a well-organized panel, you can send out a locomotive-hauled train with the original diesel trapped against the buffers. As soon as the train locomotive is clear of the first set of points you switch the platform section to the other controller and then drive the original locomotive slowly forward to come to a halt beside the starting signal, or even a little further along, ready to back into the locomotive spur to await the next train. This sort of move impresses visitors and, for the cost of about a further six switches, the same layout's operating potential is more than doubled. That is sound economy.

Finally, in Fig 5.12 I have drawn a fairly large double-track through station, which has distinct Southern (Western division) overtones, for the branch bay, complete with loop, is loosely based on Axminster, whilst the slip in the goods yard is typical LSWR practice. I think they bought a job lot and had to work them in somehow. I don't propose to discuss the arrangements in detail, I've covered most of the salient points already. Note how both the slip points have feeds, how protective isolation is installed on the main line to allow trains to be halted by signals and, in particular, how the dedicated parcels bay, where it is highly unlikely one would normally hold a locomotive, has no isolation other than that provided by the point. It's rather a jolly plan, though it needs a fair amount of room, something like a complete garage in 4mm scale. I will certainly have to develop it further.

# CHAPTER 6

# Controllers and auxiliary circuits

For most people, power supplies for the model railway are provided by a commercial unit. This is sound practice, for unless the unit is over 20 years old it has been built to a sensible, safe specification and will provide the required low voltage supplies without any risk, at a reasonable price. Where, as is generally the case, a single unit does not provide enough output for a growing layout, you simply add more boxes. It's as simple as that.

Most enthusiasts go no further, relying on one or more units of the type shown in Fig 6.1. I went into this type of controller in Chapter 1, and there is no need to recapitulate. However,

**Figure 6.1** *Typical model railway power unit*

Control knob

12 V dc Output

16 V ac Output

Metal or plastic case

this simple approach has its snags.

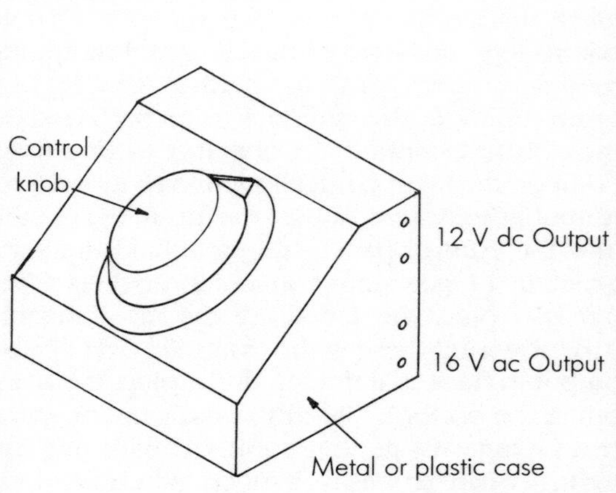

The first is that the unit is a very heavy item, because not only does it house the transformer, but, for sound safety reasons, the casing is massive enough to take heavy knocks without risk of damage. This brings the second snag, to avoid any risk of the user getting inside the case and coming in contact with 240 V ac, the case is sealed and there is usually no way of fixing it to a baseboard. I applaud the first idea, I curse the second.

Because it is a fairly large, solid unit, it cannot readily be built into a control panel. It can be located alongside, either on top of the baseboard, or, better still, on a solid shelf below the top surface. This is fine for permanent layouts, but it is bad for portable layouts since, quite apart from the weight and the difficulty of getting a secure fixing, there is the business of the trailing lead to plug in to the mains.

This brings me to the final snag. Power units come with a 'generous' two-metre long mains lead. It is too short to reach to most sockets and is invariably extended, often dangerously, turning what was intended to be a safety factor into a positive danger.

In my considered opinion, the fundamental design of model railway power units is wrong. The original concept of Meccano Ltd, when they produced the first Hornby Dublo models back in 1938, was correct. Here the controller was a separate unit from the transformer, which meant that one could place the heavy transformer on

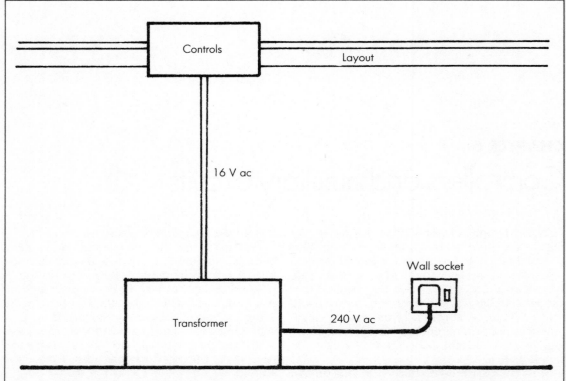

**Figure 6.2** *Block schematic of layout wiring with separate transformer standing on floor under layout*

the floor, near to the wall socket, and then carry a 16 V ac lead to the layout. This arrangement is shown schematically in Fig 6.2, and is the one I would recommend for the serious enthusiast.

Whilst it is not quite so easy to find completely shrouded transformers as one might wish, the modeller with little experience of electrical supply should be able to track some down. It is, of course, quite a simple matter to use existing power units to provide 16 V ac supplies, whilst in a later chapter I will show how to assemble a power supply which meets your specific requirements. As, initially, one rarely knows what these are, it's not a bad idea to leave this until matters are rather more developed and one has a fair idea of what one will want.

In the meantime, we need a controller. These come in several forms and, for the most part, I'd suggest you purchase a commercial unit, since these are less bother and generally cheaper than home-made equivalents. You can get separate controllers in two guises: panel-mounting modules, Fig 6.3, and hand-held devices, Fig 6.4. In my opinion, the latter are to be preferred, as they do not confine the operator to one fixed point on the layout, but allow him to move freely about the system. Whilst the modules are built into the control panel, the hand-held units are generally plugged into convenient sockets. Five-pin DIN plugs are favoured; the most suitable way of wiring these is shown in Fig 6.5. The dc output to track is at the top of the plug, the ac input at the bottom. With this arrangement, there is no danger of getting confused with left and right, as can so easily happen when working from the back of each unit. Yes, I do know that

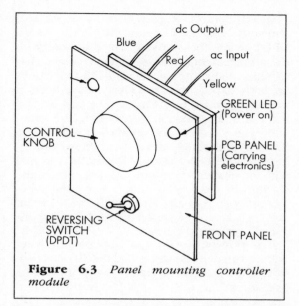

**Figure 6.3** *Panel mounting controller module*

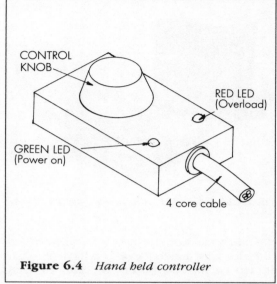

**Figure 6.4** *Hand held controller*

the terminals are numbered, but it's surprising how many experts still get it wrong.

If you want to go further, the circuit for a simple resistance controller is given in Fig 6.6. I've labelled all the parts to make life easier, and shown the transformer for good measure.

Immediately after the transformer comes the bridge rectifier. This is a network of four diodes

arranged to provide a more or less continuous dc output from an ac input. In my boyhood, these were very large copper oxide devices, with massive cooling fins which, providing you treated them carefully, might actually last a couple of years. Then came the selenium rectifiers, which still needed cooling but were very robust. I have one bought in 1946; it's as good today as it

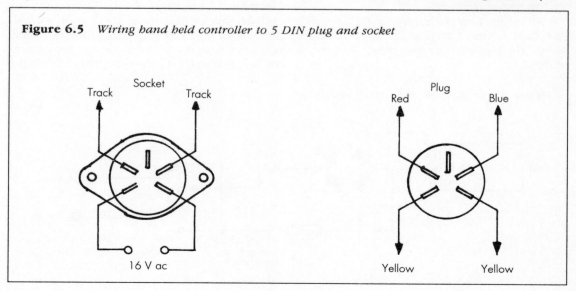

**Figure 6.5** *Wiring hand held controller to 5 DIN plug and socket*

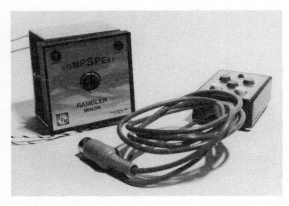

*Advanced hand-held compspeed electronic controller.*

was nearly half a century ago. Now we have very compact germanium devices which fit on to printed circuit boards, and generally need no cooling at all. They all do the same job.

Wiring bridge rectifiers is simplicity itself. The latest types have +, – and ac sine wave markings against the terminals. The older pattern, with cooling fins, have the ac input marked green, the dc output red and blue (positive and negative). Furthermore, the convention is to have the negative diodes on the outside and linked, the positive output in the centre and the ac sandwiched in between.

It is possible to replace a bridge rectifier with four diodes; this was popular for PCB work before the advent of the latest pattern of rectifiers.

Speed control is provided by a variable resistance, generally around 100 ohm, and a DPDT switch for reversing. The only snag with this arrangement is cost, since the resistance has to be able to handle high currents, and such units are fairly expensive. They always have been, it just so happened that, through the late 40s and the 1950s, a reasonable supply of ex-US Army 100 ohm Ohmite potentiometers was to be found in junk shops, and most of these came into railway modeller's hands. Do not be confused with the smaller potentiometers obtainable quite cheaply in electronics stores. Even the wire-wound pots, very rare birds by the way, are not able to take the normal current flows experienced on a model railway.

It is possible to build a stud pattern wire-wound variable resistance, and details of its construction are given in Fig 6.7, with the wiring diagram in Fig 6.8. It is a lovely turn-of-the-century design, I built such a unit some forty odd years ago, using a piece of ebonite as the base. One needs access to a lathe to make the traditional handle; all in all, it's hovering on the rim of model engineering, but on the other hand, it's strictly a scrapbox project, and accordingly cheap to make. Although many people imagine that with only 14 studs, control is a trifle jumpy, providing the resistance is approximately logarithmic, in other words, the steps at the fast end are smaller than those at the slow section, the control is remarkably good. The traditional resistance wire is a replacement coil for an electric fire; this again is something that was readily

**Figure 6.6** *Schematic diagram of resistance controller*

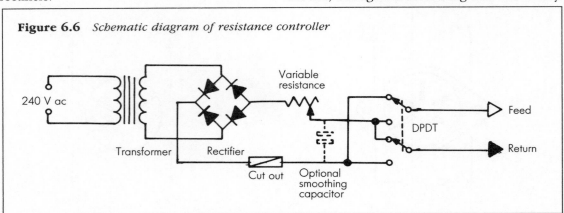

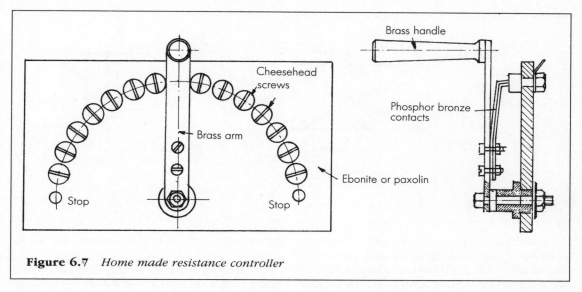

**Figure 6.7** *Home made resistance controller*

available in the 1940s but is scarce nowadays. You need to go to a specialist electrical supplier.

It is worth mentioning that the variable resistance neither wastes electricity, nor does it alter the voltage. Its action depends on Ohms law, which I do not propose to go into, but which means that the higher the current flow, the greater the voltage drop across a given resistance. So, if you measure the output of a resistance controller without a load, you will discover that you have something around 18 V on the leads. Which is a good reason for not measuring something when you don't know what it is you're measuring. In point of fact, the

output of a simple unit such as this will fall from 12 V on low load to as little as 10 V on high load with the control turned to the top setting.

Now a word about the smoothing capacitor, which is marked as optional. This acts as a rough and ready analogue of a flywheel, smoothing out the ripples in the rectified dc, and is supposed to make for better control. You need a 50 microfarad, 25 volt electrolytic capacitor, which must be correctly connected with regard to polarity, hence its location before the reverse switch. The no load reading of the unit will then be slightly over 20 V, because the capacitor charges up to the peak voltage of your half-wave.

**Figure 6.8** *Wiring diagram of home made controller*

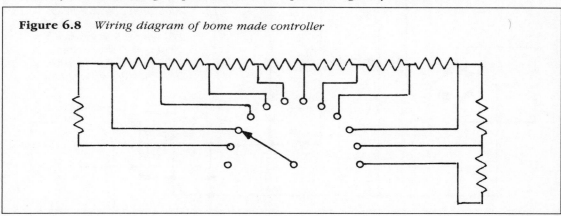

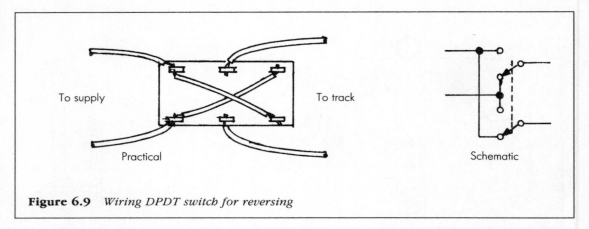

**Figure 6.9** *Wiring DPDT switch for reversing*

Smoothing isn't necessary; indeed, twenty years ago it was all the fashion to cut out most of the bridge rectifier and run the railway with half-wave power, which was supposed to provide better slow running. Like so many fashions, it has died the death.

The cut-out is a device which interrupts the supply should the current flow rise too high. It is a sort of automatic resetting fuse, and provides protection for the circuit. Today, most cut-outs are thermal, though faster acting transistorized devices are employed in electronic controllers. Many of the latest integrated circuits for control incorporate a current limiter inside the micro-chip.

The final device is a DPDT switch, preferably of the centre-off type and certainly a toggle pattern rather than the cheaper slider switch which isn't quite so happy when asked to break circuits carrying around 1 to 1.5 A. It is wired as shown in Fig 6.9.

Electronic controllers are, today, somewhat cheaper to make, since they use standard potentiometer and reasonably easily available electronic devices. A simple circuit is given in Fig 6.10. An interesting feature of this unit is that

**Figure 6.10** *Schematic diagram of simple electronic controller*

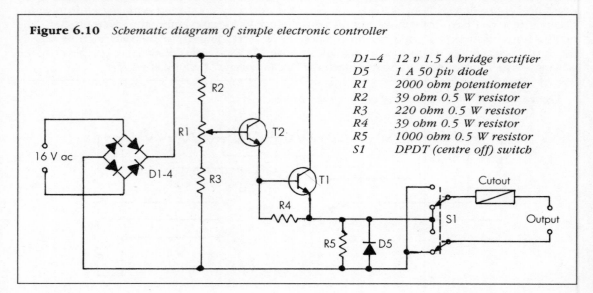

| | |
|---|---|
| D1–4 | 12 v 1.5 A bridge rectifier |
| D5 | 1 A 50 piv diode |
| R1 | 2000 ohm potentiometer |
| R2 | 39 ohm 0.5 W resistor |
| R3 | 220 ohm 0.5 W resistor |
| R4 | 39 ohm 0.5 W resistor |
| R5 | 1000 ohm 0.5 W resistor |
| S1 | DPDT (centre off) switch |

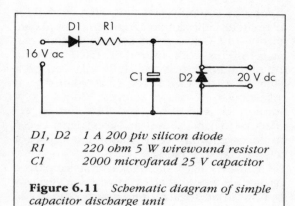

D1, D2    1 A 200 piv silicon diode
R1        220 ohm 5 W wirewound resistor
C1        2000 microfarad 25 V capacitor

**Figure 6.11** *Schematic diagram of simple capacitor discharge unit*

system in electronics, which in simple terms means that if you buy in 1000 lots your devices cost about a tenth of the price they are when bought in a bubble pack from a high street outlet. Furthermore, the commercial unit is guaranteed to work first time!

There are two devices to consider in connection with the power supply, the capacitor discharge unit for double solenoid point motors, and a smoothing circuit for relays and similar devices.

Fig 6.11 shows the basic construction of a capacitor power supply. The heart of the unit is a large electrolytic capacitor, C1, of at least 2000 microfarad and rated at 25 V dc. It is connected to the 16 V ac auxiliary supply through a diode, D1, and a ballast resistor, R1, as shown.

After around a second, the unit will be charged up to around 22 V. The reason for this is that ac is rated on its mean voltage, but the capacitor is naturally charged up to the higher peak voltage. At this point, it holds quite a useful amount of charge, and when sent through the coils of a double solenoid point motor it gives it one almighty clout. However, once the unit has discharged, the current is limited by the bleed resistor and so, as well as making sure that, providing there is no physical fault present, the point is well and truly thrown (and, moreover,

because the potentiometer has a fairly high resistance, and hence the current flow is not only low, but virtually constant, it acts as a reasonably accurate voltage divider and so, unlike the resistance controller, this unit does vary the output voltage. This is claimed to be an improvement; its value in practice is minimal.

*Amos* provides several well-tried circuits, if you are of an experimental turn of mind. However, I must point out that the moment you move beyond the most elementary of electronic controllers, it is more economical to purchase a ready-made unit. The reason lies in the pricing

**Figure 6.12** *Schematic diagram of transistor fed capacitor discharge unit*

D1–D3    1 A 200 piv silicon diode
R1        470 ohm 1 W resistor
C1        2000 microfarad 25 V capacitor
T1        NPN power transistor

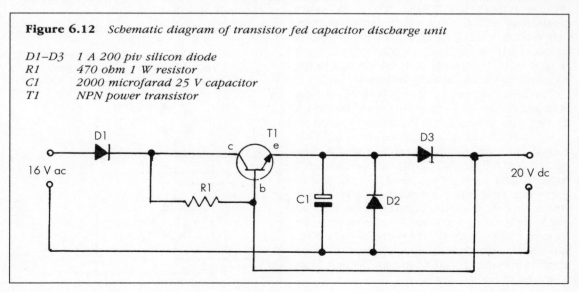

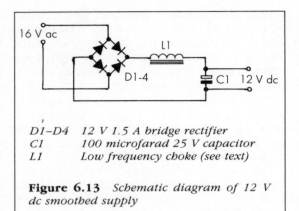

D1–D4    12 V 1.5 A bridge rectifier
C1         100 microfarad 25 V capacitor
L1         Low frequency choke (see text)

**Figure 6.13** *Schematic diagram of 12 V dc smoothed supply*

that several points can be thrown simultaneously), it prevents any damage occurring should the point switch stick.

An improved version is shown in Fig 6.12, incorporating a transistorized charge, which is considerably faster than the original elementary arrangement. I am not giving constructional details, since several manufacturers offer ready-made capacitor discharge units, and for the majority of users, these are to be preferred to a home-made device.

Whilst raw ac supplies are suitable for solenoid point motors and lighting, most model motors require dc. Where relays, or other electro-magnetic devices which are permanently powered are in use, a smoothed dc supply is essential, for the bridge rectifier supplies a rough output with a 50 Hz ripple and when connected to any coil, sets up an annoying buzz.

The basic smoothing circuit is shown in Fig 6.13 and comprises a capacitor across the output and a choke in series. The capacitor need be no more than 25 microfarad, electrolytic, of 25 V rating. The only point to note is that it is connected correctly. Small chokes are obtainable, I would advise a 2 A rating, but it isn't difficult to improvise one, since a choke is only a low-resistance coil, wound around an iron core. I've made them from the coils from broken point motors, stuffed with short lengths of steel wire. It is usually a good idea to incorporate the bridge rectifier into the unit so it can take its input from a standard 16 V ac supply.

For a 24 V supply, which is often needed for relay circuits, the simplest arrangement is to connect two 12 V dc supplies in series, as shown in Fig 6.14. This works even if the rated output of the two transformers isn't fully matched, as is likely to be the case if you've assembled your collection from various sources. Where a 32 V transformer is available, and 24 V bridge rectifiers are to hand, all well and good: Fig 6.14 can be followed, but your smoothing capacitor needs to be 50 V rating.

There are voltage-doubling circuits employed in some electronic devices. As you don't get owt for nowt in electrical matters, any more than you do in the rest of the world, such circuits effectively halve the current capacity of the supply. As we generally need all the amps we can get, I do not advise this ingenious approach.

I should mention that these smoothing circuits are comparatively crude, and are only intended to remove the ac hum from relays and other coils. For electronic applications you require a regulated voltage output, which used to require a lot of complicated devices, but is now dealt with by integrated circuits. These are rather beyond the scope of this book, but are covered in *Amos*.

**Figure 6.14** *Schematic diagram of 24 V dc smoothed supply*

D1–D4    12 V 1.5 A bridge rectifier
D5–D8    12 V 1.5 A bridge rectifier
C1         1000 microfarad 50 V capacitor
L1         Low frequency choke (see text)

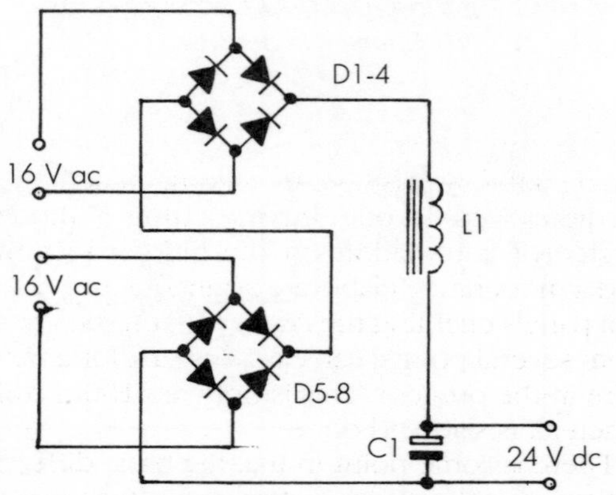

# CHAPTER 7

# Tag strips and control panels

It's now time to leave theory for a little, and get down to the nuts and bolts of wiring the layout, but before we do so, I must emphasize that there are differing schools of thought on the subject. The system I'm advocating is the one I've arrived at by practical experiment over the years, and one I consider simple to install and, more important still, simple to modify and debug. The underlying principle is to use tag strip to locate the wires and to provide a means of identification which is simple, positive and readily recorded.

I am not greatly in favour of full colour coding. It has its uses, particularly where multicore wires are concerned, but in order to make full use of the system it is necessary to purchase far more wire than you will actually need since there is no way of predicting, in advance, exactly how much of any particular colour is going to be used.

Even if money is no object, there are far more worthy ways of squandering it around a model railway than on a kilometre of unnecessary wire. Incidentally, whilst we're talking of length, a medium-sized layout, incorporating a modest degree of automation on the hidden sections, and a moderately elaborate arrangement of control panels enabling the owner to run the layout from several points, can easily use a kilometre of wire in the process. This is only ten 100m coils, when all is said and done.

There is some point in making basic differentiation by colour. For a start, the return can be through bare copper wire, salvaged from twin plus earth mains cable, or bought separately. This needs to be of heavy cross-section, since several separate circuits will share this wire and unless you use something around 16 SWG or 1mm$^2$ wire, you may get voltage drop. By the same token, you must use a reasonable thickness of wire for any long feed, or once again voltage drop may rear its ugly head.

Although we tend to assume that a copper wire has no resistance, or, if we think deeply, a negligible resistance, this isn't so. It has a very low resistance per metre, but when you get several metres of thin wire, with a relatively high resistance, as conductors go, then you can end up with a sizeable fraction of an ohm. If you are passing a current of around 1 A, then this resistance is not entirely negligible at 12 V dc, and you lose some of your voltage. Losing 1 volt on 240 V is neither here nor there, but loosing 1 V when you have effectively reduced your nominal 12 V to no more than 8 V for slow running is very serious. I'll have more to say about this in the troubleshooting chapter. For the time being, it's worth pointing out that voltage drop is less of a problem in the 1980s than it was in the 1930s, when O gauge locomotives needed 3 A and layouts were larger. But it is essential when wiring a layout to use thick enough wire.

A simple and adequate colour coding has the 12 V controlled feeds in colour – any colour – whilst ac feeds to point motors can be white, leaving black for low-voltage lighting. This can

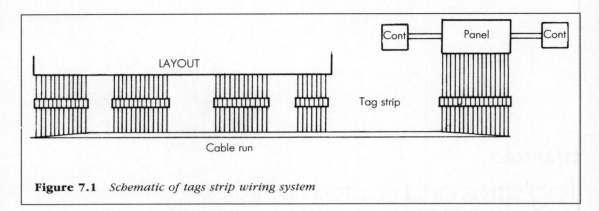

**Figure 7.1** *Schematic of tags strip wiring system*

be helpful, but in practice, sooner or later, one hooks in a 'temporary' circuit with the wrong colour, and leaves it in place, or, more often, just runs out of the chosen colour of wire. A hundred metre drum looks ample, but as I pointed out above, we do use a lot of wire on our layouts.

The tag strip system obviates any real need to maintain colour coding, since the tagstrips provide not only a means of identification, but useful places to check the continuity of circuits; again this is dealt with in Chapter 15.

The basic principle is that wires are taken from the track to a nearby tag strip, then further wires are taken from tagstrips to the control panel tagstrip. This is shown schematically in Fig 7.1.

Each tag strip is numbered. In general it is only necessary to identify No 1 with a blob of paint, as shown in Fig 7.2. Where large arrays are involved, it helps to notch off the tens. Most important of all, a record of each tag strip and its function is kept, preferably in a wiring book. The wiring book is generally a cheap notebook; the best are those with squared grids. In this we list which circuit connects to which tag strip. A simple wiring diagram is usually included.

Of course, each tag strip needs to be identified. The letters of the alphabet ought to suffice; if not, use two letters. I favour self-adhesive labels for marking, they are easily obtainable and easily crossed out should you need to make changes. I would advise a good permanent ink, rather than ball-point or typewritten labels, as these last two tend to fade with age.

In this chapter we shall be considering permanent layouts, which, on the face of it are easier to wire. There is just one small difficulty: conventional thought suggests that the wiring is done *under* the baseboard. If you like lying on your

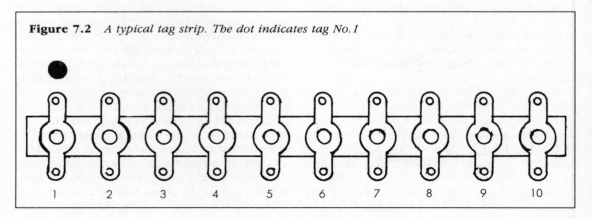

**Figure 7.2** *A typical tag strip. The dot indicates tag No.1*

back with a soldering iron above you and you are happy with the ever-present risk of hot solder falling on your face, so be it. I dislike the idea intensely.

I have included some photographs of layout modules wired, through multi-core cables, to tag strips. With this arrangement, the points and point motors (in this instance, relays) are assembled on the workbench, fully wired to the tag strip and tested before installing on the layout. As around 80 per cent of the wiring is concentrated around the point formations, this greatly reduces the amount of wiring needed on

**Figure 7.3** *Wiring a permanent layout without soldering beneath the baseboard*

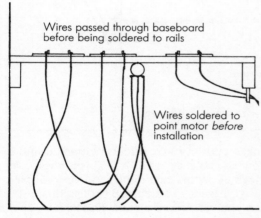

Wires passed through baseboard before being soldered to rails

Wires soldered to point motor *before* installation

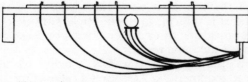

Wires taken to tag strip, cut to length, bared and soldered

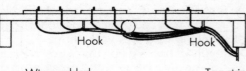

Hook                    Hook

Wires cabled                    Tag strip

the layout itself. These photographs also give a fairly good idea of how wiring can be undertaken without producing a complete cat's cradle of wires.

This system is intended for open-top baseboard construction and is, in my opinion, as good an argument for this form of construction on permanent layouts as the more usual claims for better scenic modelling.

If you require a solid top baseboard, I suggest that you follow a slightly different method, which is shown in Fig 7.3. Here the tag strips are located on the baseboard framing and lengths of wire are cut to reach generously from the connecting point to the nearest tag strip. Don't be niggardly, for whilst you can easily shorten a wire, it is a considerable nuisance trying to lengthen it. It can be done, but the resulting splice is a point of weakness and a potential source of trouble.

For track connections, drill a hole beside the track, poke the wire through until only about 100mm is left above the baseboard. Bare the last 3 to 4mm of the wire, tin the end and then bend it at right angles, push the remainder through until the bared and tinned end is alongside the rail and solder it in place. Now loosely carry the under-baseboard length around your hooks or holes to the tag strip, shorten it, bare the end and solder it to the appropriate tag strip. It is best to put one wire in at a time, checking that you have made the right connection. If you wait until you've wired in a couple of dozen, you'll have a lovely time sorting out which is which!

The best method of checking is shown in Fig 7.4. You need a cheap multimeter, set to the resistance reading. You place one of the two probes on the length of rail you think you're connecting, and brush the other across the bared end of the wire. When the needle swings completely over, you know you've got the right wire. Connect it to the required tag strip and then proceed to the next. Either connect in accordance with a pre-determined arrangement, which is best, or record the wiring details as you go along. Don't do this on a scrap of paper: one reason for using a wiring book is that it is a lot less easy to mislay, or even throw away.

Clearly, whilst this works well for connections

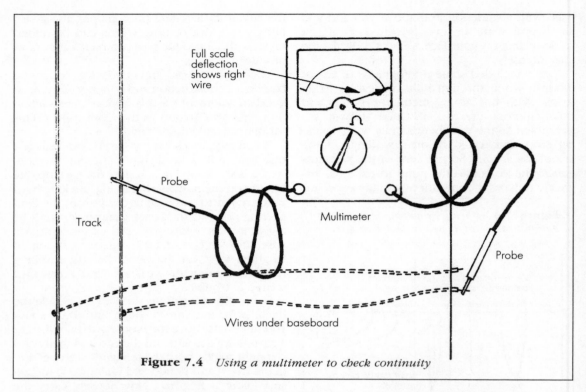

Full scale
deflection
shows right
wire

Probe

Track

Multimeter

Probe

Wires under baseboard

**Figure 7.4**  *Using a multimeter to check continuity*

made above the baseboard, some devices are mounted underneath: point motors are the most common example. The obvious answer is to solder the wires to the unit before you mount it under the baseboard. Screwing a point motor in place from underneath is not too difficult a task, providing you drill pilot holes for the screws. But you always do that, don't you?

As you proceed, you'll begin to create a mess of wires between the various odds and ends. If you leave it like this, access to the underside is going to get progressively more and more difficult so, whilst the wiring works, alterations to the layout will become more and more difficult. The correct answer is cabling.

A cable is made by bringing a number of wires together in a nice smooth batch and joining them together. You can buy special plastic clips for this purpose; they look neat and professional, but they cost money and cannot be reused. Initially you can produce cables simply and economically by using short (50–75mm

long) sections of wire offcuts twisted around the growing cable, as in Fig 7.5. This is cheap, very tidy (it clears up the offcuts) and very simple.

If you want to add a real professional touch, then you use waxed thread. This isn't easily obtained; modern quick shoe repairers rarely undertake to stitch leather as the old cobblers used to, and so a convenient source of the material is difficult to track down. However, if you run strong thread over a block of beeswax, you get the same result.

The purpose of the wax is to help stick the thread together. Fig 7.6 shows a cable correctly threaded; note the slightly involved knot at each loop – the simple hitch shown in the inset is not a lot of good, as it tends to pull apart. The technique is relatively easy to learn, and the result is not only very neat and professional, but also impresses anyone who sees your wiring.

Once you've hooked up your wires to the tag strips, you need to connect the tag strips to the panels, or occasionally, to each other. Once

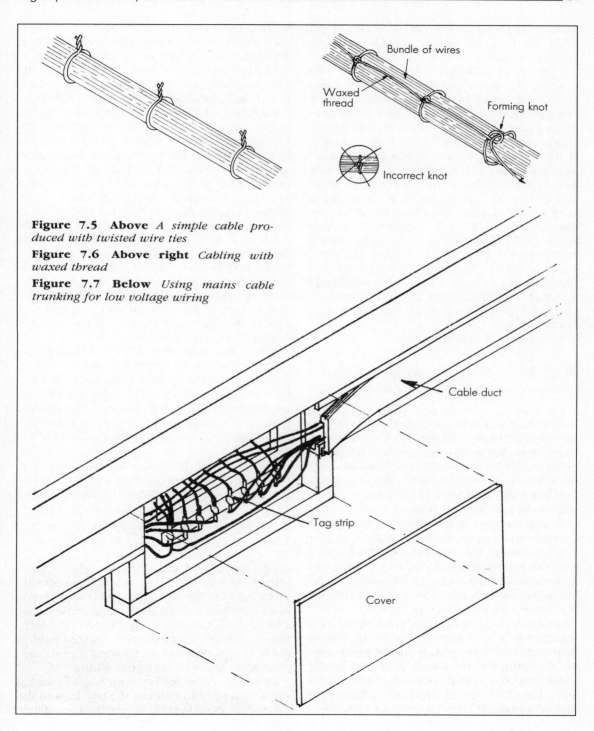

**Figure 7.5 Above** *A simple cable produced with twisted wire ties*

**Figure 7.6 Above right** *Cabling with waxed thread*

**Figure 7.7 Below** *Using mains cable trunking for low voltage wiring*

again, you create cables, and you can, if you wish, fix these to further hooks along the baseboard edge.

There is an alternative. Any large DIY store catering for home wiring can supply plastic trunking designed to hold mains cables neatly in place on the surface of a wall. This consists of a C shaped base with a snap-in cover, and will just take two lengths of twin 2.5mm plus earth cable. It will also take at least 50 low voltage wires, depending on just how tidily you put the wires in the cable housing. Finally, if you make simple wooden covers for the tag strips, you end up with a readily accessible wiring system that looks extremely neat, as Fig 7.7 shows. As an alternative to the wooden covers, the wall-mounting patrass sold to take twin 13 A sockets, together with the special plastic covers that are used for blanking unwanted outlets, may be used. It adds about a fiver, but the result is very neat and looks extremely professional. It all depends on your budget.

To sum up, we need another rule:

## RULE 11    Keep all wires neatly cabled or enclosed in a cable duct.

You can, if you wish, use multi-core cable, or ribbon cable to connect the tag strips. It appears to be fairly costly, but when you work out just how much wire you need, the difference can be quite small. A more serious objection is that you'll be very lucky to find a cable with precisely the correct number of cores for the job, and then the cable does become appreciably more costly – unless you happen upon it as scrap.

Occasionally, the shortest distance between two major connections is between baseboards and across an operating well. In such cases it is absolutely essential to ensure that the cable duct is securely covered, and that there is no chance of an accident, to the cable or to the users. This is so awkward that I would only advise this approach where a very large number of wires have to be carried across a gap, and it is not too difficult to get them under the floor. In most cases, this means a loft layout, where the cables can be loosely carried between a pair of joists. This is

where a multi-core or ribbon cable is well worth the extra cost, since a few spare wires for future developments are well worth including.

Control panels take many forms. There are two opposing schools of thought, the local board and the Mighty Wurlitzer. Most newcomers think lovingly of the centralized panel, largely because the larger, more impressive exhibition layouts have such devices. Where the layout is big and there are plenty of operators and, most important of all, there are at least two people who understand the intricacies of the system, the central panel does make sense. However, as it is likely to be some distance away from any part of the layout, the amount of wire required is considerable and so the cost is fairly high. The local panel is simpler, and is certainly a better proposition for the beginner. It is also decidedly cheaper. It must be emphasized that with tag strip wiring it is possible to begin with a series of small local panels and progress to a Mighty Wurlitzer and beyond, if the layout is suitable for such treatment.

There are, again, two schools of thought on panel design, the geographical and the in-line. The geographical system looks good, is fairly easy to follow, and greatly resembles modern prototype practice, but has one ineradicable fault: any change in the layout plan means a reconstruction, if not a complete rebuild of the panel.

To get round this particular snag there have been several commercial mosaic pattern panels, where the various switches and indicators are ar-

*A very simple local control panel. The socket in the centre is for a plug-in hand-held controller.*

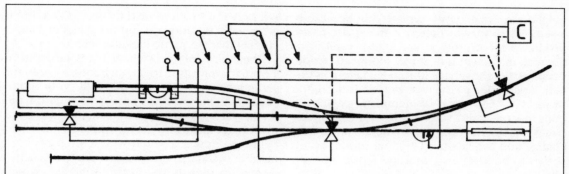

**Figure 7.8**  *Full wiring diagram of small terminus*

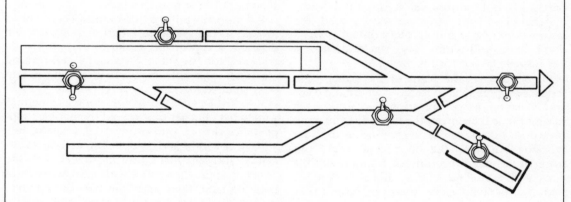

**Figure 7.9**  *A geographic control panel for the small terminus*

**Figure 7.10**  *Rear of control panel showing wiring*

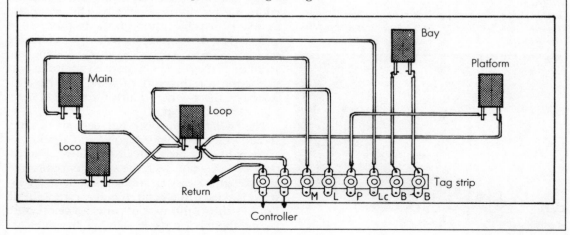

ranged on small units which can be readily assembled in varying patterns. Such patterns are produced for prototype use, and several Continental manufacturers have produced model versions, but these have not gained favour in Britain, largely due to the cost factors. Indeed, the majority of prototype diagrammatic panels are built in large units, since even with the mosaic panel, it is still necessary to rewire the unit after a change and the favoured system, model or full size, is to build a new panel and replace the old one.

The small branch terminus of chapter 5 turns up again in Fig 7.8, where the basic feeds and breaks symbols are translated into a full wiring diagram. The feed wires are shown solid, the return dotted; it is immediately obvious why I don't favour full wiring diagrams, and chose a very simple layout for my example.

Fig 7.9 shows the front of the panel, with toggle switches located roughly where the feeds and isolating loops are shown on the track diagram. The panel front is best made from 4mm plywood. I did use sheet melamine, as used for working surfaces, but in recent years this material has been made much thinner, and the current breed is far too flimsy. If it is stuck to ply with a suitable adhesive, then you have a very pleasant panel. I don't recommend aluminium;

*An example of a control panel backed by a diagram. This particular example was on the Basle Model Railway Club's extensive Gauge 1 system, the similarity to a full sized panel is intentional.*

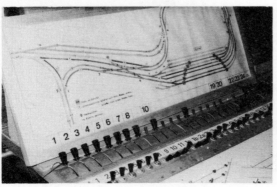

not only is it much more difficult to work, but it is a conductor and you can get accidental short circuits that are particularly difficult to trace.

The holes for the switches will range from 12mm for miniature toggle switches, to 7mm for sub-miniature types; check with your components. The switches have two nuts on the threaded ferrule: the back nut is adjusted to leave the top nut flush with the top of the ferrule when tightened down. Tighten well with a small adjustable spanner, as you don't want the switches turning in their holes. Rotary switches, which are prone to move, have a small tag: drill a 3mm hole for this, taking care to ensure the correct alignment of the pointer knob.

If your panel is not to look ungainly, you need to take scrupulous care when marking out the diagram. It is probably easier to use 6mm wide coloured adhesive tape. That sold for embossing machines is suitable, particularly as you can emboss suitable legends, e.g. PLATFORM 1, BAY, LOCO SHED, GOODS LOOP along its length. A somewhat cheaper tape is sold by graphics suppliers for diverse purposes, and is available in a variety of widths and colours. If you have an airbrush, you can first spray the panel with the 'track' colour, then mask with narrow strips of masking tape, then spray the base colour over the lot. When dry, the masking tape will reveal a very neat, professional looking panel. The same result can be achieved with two contrasting cans of spray paint.

Fig 7.10 shows the rear of the panel with the wiring shown diagrammatically. The only point to note is that since the loco shed isolator takes its feed directly from the loop feed, we eliminate one connection to the layout by linking the switches at the panel. On more elaborate layouts the scope for this sort of thing can be considerable; this is where a little forethought saves a good deal of effort.

The in-line panel does not get out of date, should you revise your layout, and although it appears to be more difficult to follow, a signal-box type diagram, with the switches numbered accordingly, is easy to arrange, simple to understand and easy to amend. It is also prototypical. Fig 7.11 shows this type of panel for our pattern layout; there is a considerable gain in simplicity,

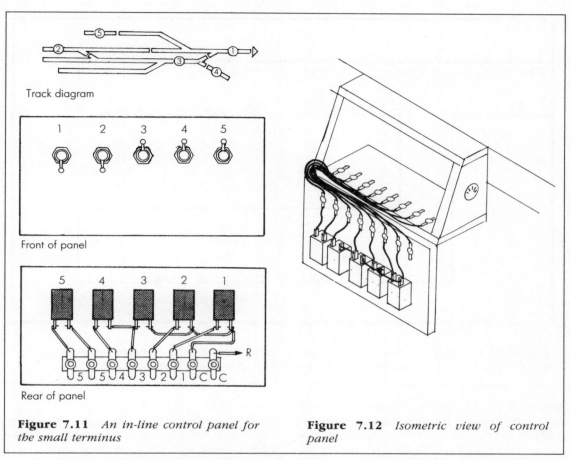

**Figure 7.11** *An in-line control panel for the small terminus*

**Figure 7.12** *Isometric view of control panel*

though it has to be admitted that the first panel looks more impressive.

Whichever system is followed, the wiring from the switches is taken to tag strips. It is essential to allow for access behind the panel. This is generally done by hinging the front to the main frame, and allowing it to swing open. In most cases, the hinges are arranged so that the panel is at rest in both open and closed positions; in this way, no fixings or struts are required. The general design shown in Fig 7.12 is preferred where the panel is near to the vertical. If it is nearer the horizontal, then the hinge is on the far side. This arrangement is more suited to the larger panel, and in such cases, a piano hinge is required if the panel is not to twist.

There is, on the side of the panel, a five-pin DIN socket for a hand-held controller. This type of controller is growing in popularity because it enables the operator to move around the layout rather than forcing him to stand in one place, glumly looking at his layout from one angle. This can be developed into full walkaround control, where the operator or operators follow their trains around the system, changing points and energizing sections from small panels. The system is easiest followed from Fig 7.13, which shows a fairly typical arrangement for an extensive system.

Whilst most privately-owned layouts are fairly small and straightforward, there are exceptions, where the enthusiast has a reasonable amount of space at his disposal, together with enough spare time and, above all, available funds to finance a

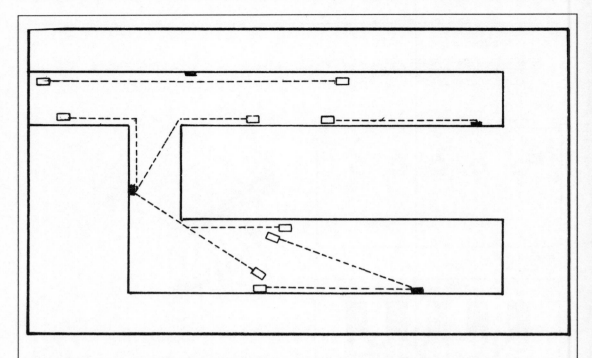

**Figure 7.13** *Block diagram of walkaround control. With only four plug-in locations for the controller, an operator can stand alongside any part of a large system*

large system. In such cases, there can be virtues in the Mighty Wurlitzer approach, possibly with a large master panel from which the entire layout can be controlled, in a limited fashion, by one man, with subsidiary panels for local control and operation by a group. If the more elaborate system is developed as the layout matures, all well and good. Not only will the owner have acquired a sound practical knowledge of layout wiring techniques, but, more important still, he will have a far better idea of the way his layout should be operated. In addition, it is more than probable that a support group of close friends will have been built up to share the work and help run the model. Providing this is allowed to develop naturally, there will be no problems, so long as the tag strip system has been followed. As I hope I have managed to show, it offers a great degree of flexibility, since it is quite simple, working from the front of the layout, to modify the control arrangements, or to fit extra features

into the general scheme of things.

Good control systems evolve from simple beginnings. One should never attempt to create a large, elaborate control system without a lot of practical experience; that way only leads to costly mistakes that produce a layout that simply will not function. Equally, it is unwise to commission someone else to build one for you. Whilst this can be done, at a price, there is an even larger hidden cost. Should it go wrong, only the original builder has a hope of putting things right, and even he may well have forgotten exactly why certain circuits are the way they are.

In short, cultivate simplicity; it's cheaper, and generally gives far better value. Or, to make it a little more formal:

**RULE 12**  Always keep the wiring as simple as you can to achieve the required effect.

# CHAPTER 8

# Wiring for portability

Portable layouts pose special problems when it comes to their electrification, but they have one very distinct advantage: you can stand them on their side and wire them from underneath in complete comfort. Indeed, because so many club and private layouts are built in sections, a good deal of modern British wiring techniques rely on the ability to present the baseboard in this convenient fashion. So, although we will

*Even a large portable section, such as those used on a club layout, is easy to wire when stood on edge.*

now be dealing with a number of special arrangements, you should never lose sight of the fact that it is a great deal easier to get at the wiring on a portable layout.

There are many approaches to the problems posed by the baseboard joints, but there is only one single common factor that must be observed. Never, ever, under any provocation, let a section break fall across a baseboard joint. There is a good deal of movement here, and sooner or later the rails which you think are safely apart, come into contact. Worse still, this is an erratic contact, and accordingly, difficult to pin-point. This brings us to yet another rule:

**RULE 13** Never let a section break coincide with a baseboard joint.

We should begin by considering the important matter of carrying electrical circuits across baseboard joints. The simple method is to provide matching pairs of inter-baseboard contacts. These consist of strips of springy brass or bronze, measuring approximately 6mm wide by 30–40mm long. They are either soldered directly to rail ends, to complete the circuits across track joints, or else just pinned to the baseboard ends where additional leads need to be taken across. The system is shown in Fig 8.1.

The main problem is tracking down the springy material, but if you can find a DIY store selling phosphor bronze draught excluder strip, you're home and dried. This used to be readily

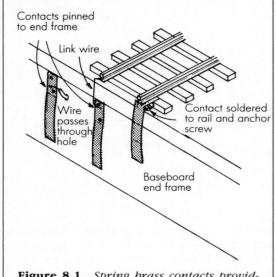

**Figure 8.1** *Spring brass contacts providing electrical continuity across baseboard joints*

available in Woolworths under the trade name 'Atomic'; I bought some a few years back, and in all probability the material is still around since, unlike the plastic foam pattern, it really does last. One roll will provide you with all the contacts you're ever likely to need.

These contacts are vulnerable, but so are the track ends, and therefore it is a good idea to have cover boards which bolt on the ends. It's an even better idea if the cover boards are so arranged that they hold a pair of baseboards about 300mm apart, face to face, forming a simple crate which protects the models as well. The same spacer boards also allow you to invert a baseboard on the bench to get at the underside for wiring.

This arrangement is excellent for truly portable layouts, but is less effective where the layout stands erected for any length of time. There are two snags. The first is that the baseboards tend to move apart, and contact can become erratic. At the same time dust and dirt falls between the contacts, with the result that things don't work when they should. A simple cure is to slide a very long, thin nail file down

between the contacts and then pull the sections together.

The alternative arrangement is multi-pin plugs and sockets. This is more costly and time-consuming to arrange, but much more positive in use. There are four ways of using these devices, three of which are shown in Fig 8.2.

The simplest arrangement is to have a socket on one section and a plug on a lead on the other, as shown in the upper diagram. Unfortunately a dangling lead, even a relatively short one, is a positive menace and so this arrangement is not too good where the layout goes up and down fairly frequently.

The jumper cable shown in the middle diagram is very popular in clubs, where, for exhibition layouts, cost is of secondary importance to simplicity in use. With a single type of jumper lead, there is no need to mark the plugs and sockets: any jumper fits any joint. There are two snags with this system: you need twice as many

**Figure 8.2** *Three ways of arranging jumper cables across a baseboard joint*

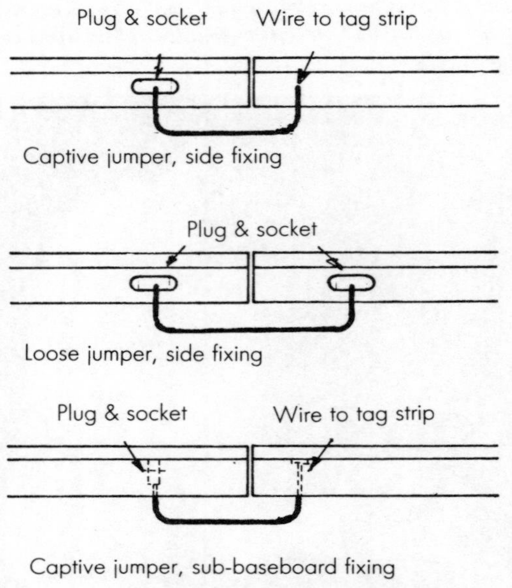

Plug & socket    Wire to tag strip

Captive jumper, side fixing

Plug & socket

Loose jumper, side fixing

Plug & socket    Wire to tag strip

Captive jumper, sub-baseboard fixing

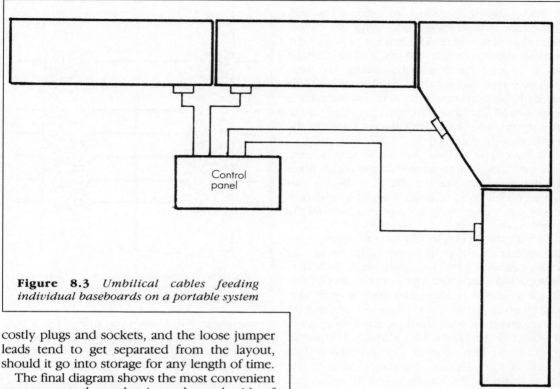

**Figure 8.3** *Umbilical cables feeding individual baseboards on a portable system*

costly plugs and sockets, and the loose jumper leads tend to get separated from the layout, should it go into storage for any length of time.

The final diagram shows the most convenient arrangement, the socket is on the underside of the baseboard and the jumper is similarly secured to the other baseboard. A suitable sized Terry clip is screwed to the second baseboard to hold the cable whilst in transit. It's fairly cheap and reasonably foolproof.

The final approach is the umbilical cord. With this arrangement, the control panel is separate, and couples directly to each section through a suitable multi-way cable, as shown in Fig 8.3. As 25-pin connectors are readily available (they're used for computers and similar devices) it is relatively easy to connect quite a complex system to a central panel. Furthermore, for exhibition use, the panel can be taken to the other side of the terminus-fiddle yard scheme, so that the visitors get the best view of the model.

Making a multi-way connection is not too difficult, providing you go about it methodically. The first thing to decide upon is whether you are going to buy multi-core cable, which tends to be

fairly costly, or make up your own. However, as a 100 metre coil will only make a 4m-long 25-way cable, the ready-made cable is not quite as expensive as it seems at first sight, bearing in mind the fact that you're going to need some form of shrouding around the wires at the end of the day.

There are three possible ways of arranging this. One is a woven cover, which stretches to fit snugly over your cable. The snag with this is that you have to guess how far it will shorten as it stretches to contain your wires, and furthermore, you have to fit it before you put on the plugs.

The other systems are applied afterwards. One uses a spiral of plastic which is wound around the wires. Once again, it shortens as you increase the effective diameter of the cable, but as you wind it in from a coil, it's not too difficult to cut it to length at the end. It is fairly costly, however.

The cheapest solution is to cable it yourself. There are two methods, one using fine twine, the other plastic tape. The latter is probably the easiest: you secure one end of the cable, take the slack in one hand whilst winding the self-adhesive tape around the wires in a spiral. This needs to be done carefully, as unless the trailing edge is well firmed down on the previous part of the spriral, you soon get a gooey mess on the outside of the cable.

Waxed twine, rather than thread, can be used to create a cable in the same fashion as described in the previous chapter (Fig 7.6). Whilst this doesn't look quite so neat, it is cheap and very easily taken apart with a sharp knife, should the need arise.

Where the layout, whilst built in sections, remains erected for 95 per cent of the time, and only comes down for high days, holidays, redecorating and exhibitions, a very simple way of carrying power across the joints is to fit matching sets of tag strips on either side of the joint and to link these with short pieces of wire, cut to a uniform length and soldered across. It is simple to cut these with a pair of wire cutters and then re-solder new lengths, but there remains the tricky business of soldering uphill. An alternative is to use matching sets of screw connections, slightly more expensive initially, but much easier

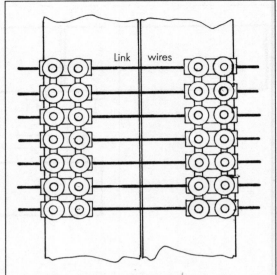

**Figure 8.4** *Connections across joints on a semi-permanent sectioned layout*

to dismantle. I've shown this in Fig 8.4. It is, in theory, possible to make this type of connection fairly painless by setting the two connectors close together, say 10mm maximum, and making the connections with short lengths of heavy gauge copper wire. The earth wire from the mains cable is ideal. Clearly, it is essential to close

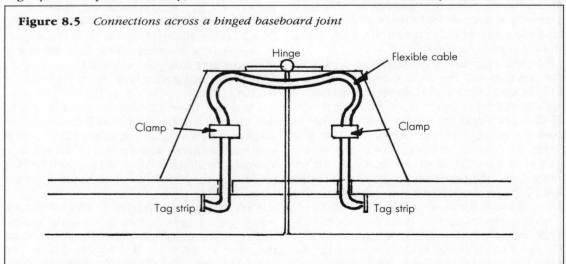

**Figure 8.5** *Connections across a hinged baseboard joint*

the baseboard joint with absolute precision, probably using coach bolts in metal tubes to align the two sections. If it works, it's marvellous, but should only one wire bend, the result is little short of catastrophic; you get a mysterious short circuit that virtually defies detection.

Where portable baseboards hinge, a flexible cable has to be provided at the hinged joint. Fig 8.5 shows a good way, with the cable running inside the hinged joint. It is, of course, advisable to provide some form of scenic cover in this case. The cable must be made with multi-strand flexible wire; solid core will break in no time at all. It needs to be neatly cabled and there should be plenty of slack at the hinge to allow the baseboards to be closed without straining the wire, or causing all the flexing to occur in the same short length of wire.

Whilst separate control panels are very simple to arrange, it is often rather difficult to provide adequate support. One answer, where the panel is housed in a reasonably large box, is to fit a set of screw-in legs, obtainable from any DIY store, and produce what is in effect, a coffee table control panel. An alternative arrangement is shown in Fig 8.6, where our old friend the small terminus crops up again. The control panel is held on the side of the baseboard by a pair of slotted metal brackets, sliding over roundhead screws. A twin flex lead goes to the floor-mounted transformer, whilst a multi-pin plug and socket, on a very short lead, plugs into the layout. A five pin DIN socket is provided on the side for the hand-held controller. This is simple and highly convenient.

Another answer, shown in Fig 8.7, is to house a very compact in-line panel in the back of a substantial building at the edge of the baseboard. Once again we have the five switches for our tiny terminus, plus a controller module.

Fig 8.8 shows in block form yet another possibility for the small portable layout. Here the

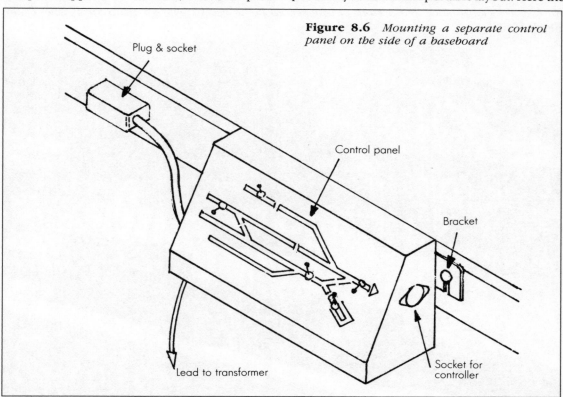

**Figure 8.6** *Mounting a separate control panel on the side of a baseboard*

Plug & socket

Control panel

Bracket

Lead to transformer

Socket for controller

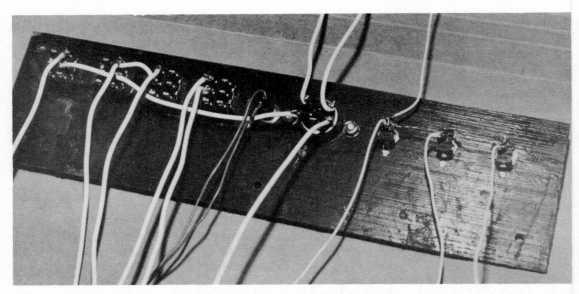

*Rear of simple control panel showing the straightforward wiring.*

*An ex-govt. switch block and a band of commercial point levers comprises the control panel of this simple layout.*

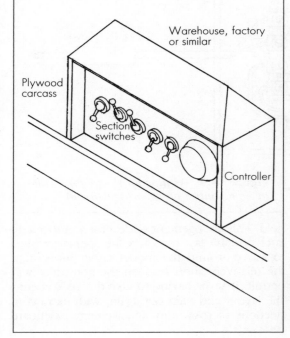

**Figure 8.7** *A compact control panel housed in a lineside building*

*Wiring beneath a portable layout, with a circular multi-pin socket for connection directly to the control panel.*

*A bank of ex-RAF bomb release switches makes a compact control panel for a small portable layout.*

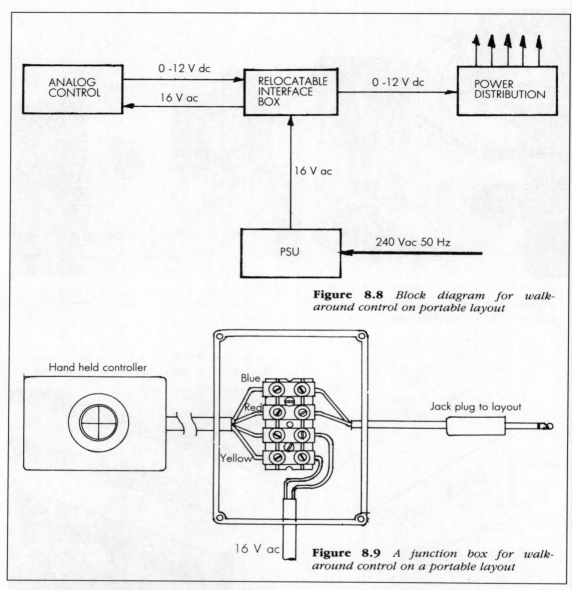

**Figure 8.8** *Block diagram for walk-around control on portable layout*

**Figure 8.9** *A junction box for walk-around control on a portable layout*

hand-held controller terminates in a small plastic junction box, which has two outlets, a long twin flex which goes to the transformer, and a short twin cable, terminating in a 3.5mm jack plug, which plugs into the layout, as shown in Fig 8.9. A strip of Velcro, cemented to the back, with a matching strip alongside the jack socket on the baseboard side, allows the box to be securely held. This arrangement is ideal for a moderately large portable layout, where the operator wishes to move around the model rather more than the relatively short lead on the controller will permit. It saves having to take the 16 V ac into the layout and then out again, with extra connections across any intervening baseboard joints.

# CHAPTER 9

# Reverse loops and triangles

There are two useful track formations that give a lot of trouble in two-rail wiring: triangles and reverse loops. They are a convenient way of turning complete trains end from end but, in the process of doing this, ensure that the feed and return rails meet. Which, as you will recall from Rule 3, is not on.

What do we do? Well, we could just put a double rail break in the middle, which would prevent trouble, until we tried to take a train over it. Then the fun would really begin . . . the locomotive would bridge the gap, neatly shorting out the circuit. It would stop, because the cut-out had been blown.

The basic way of getting over this difficulty is to insert a section roughly one train's length, or as near to that as you can get, and feed that through a separate reversing switch, as shown in Fig 9.1. All you have to do then is to stop the train on the reversing section, throw the switch, and then drive out on the other route. This process is shown, step by step, in Fig 9.2. The fact that the train has to stop is a definite snag.

The triangle also needs a reverse feed. It requires a little extra consideration since, unlike the reverse loop, which is extremely uncommon on the prototype and is mainly confined to rapid transport systems and tramways, the triangular junction is quite common.

It exists for one of two reasons. The first is rather unusual in British practice, but extremely common in the USA. It would probably be popular in Europe but for the fact that, long before railways came on the scene, the place was not only crowded, but all the land had an owner. When a train arrives at its terminus, it has to turn round and come back. It is far more convenient if it doesn't have to go to all that trouble, and whilst a complete reverse loop does this very efficiently, it takes up a great deal of room if the curves are easy enough to handle large locomotives and coaches. However, a triangle is a lot less obtrusive and so in the USA, reversing wyes were installed at many termini. There was usually plenty of room and, once the line got out of the settled Eastern seaboard, the company usually owned the land into the bargain. Building a railroad is a lot easier if there are no inhabitants to argue the toss over where it should go. The 'not in my back yard' syndrome predated motorways by well over a century.

This type of triangle is relatively easy to electrify for one reason: the train has to stop at the end of the odd leg. So we can easily arrange electrification with the feed as shown in Fig 9.3 and, what is more to the point, link the reverse feed to the point. Indeed, there is a way of wiring this very elementary arrangement so that the points select the correct polarity, but this tends to go wrong the moment you depart from the elementary turning wye, which is, as I've suggested, a rather unusual feature in European practice. The more common arrangement is the triangular junction. This can be dealt with in the same fashion, but there is a better arrangement, which I shall deal with later.

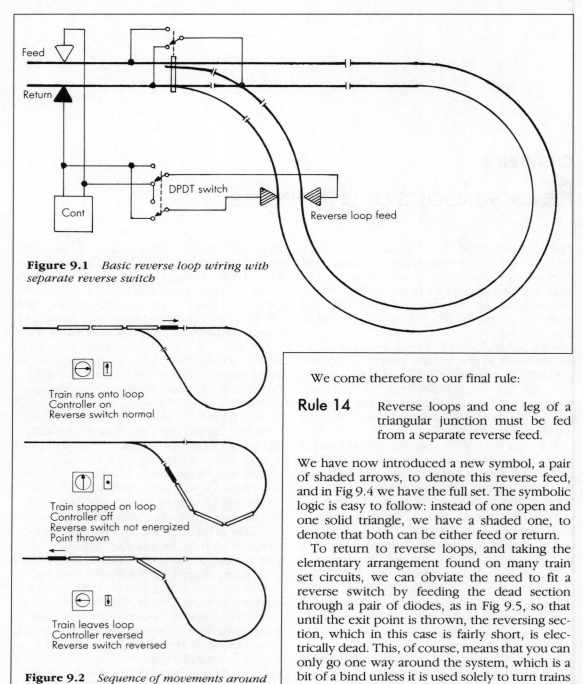

**Figure 9.1** *Basic reverse loop wiring with separate reverse switch*

Train runs onto loop
Controller on
Reverse switch normal

Train stopped on loop
Controller off
Reverse switch not energized
Point thrown

Train leaves loop
Controller reversed
Reverse switch reversed

**Figure 9.2** *Sequence of movements around a reverse loop*

We come therefore to our final rule:

**Rule 14**  Reverse loops and one leg of a triangular junction must be fed from a separate reverse feed.

We have now introduced a new symbol, a pair of shaded arrows, to denote this reverse feed, and in Fig 9.4 we have the full set. The symbolic logic is easy to follow: instead of one open and one solid triangle, we have a shaded one, to denote that both can be either feed or return.

To return to reverse loops, and taking the elementary arrangement found on many train set circuits, we can obviate the need to fit a reverse switch by feeding the dead section through a pair of diodes, as in Fig 9.5, so that until the exit point is thrown, the reversing section, which in this case is fairly short, is electrically dead. This, of course, means that you can only go one way around the system, which is a bit of a bind unless it is used solely to turn trains back into a terminus station off the main line. As with many of these ingenious arrangements, we

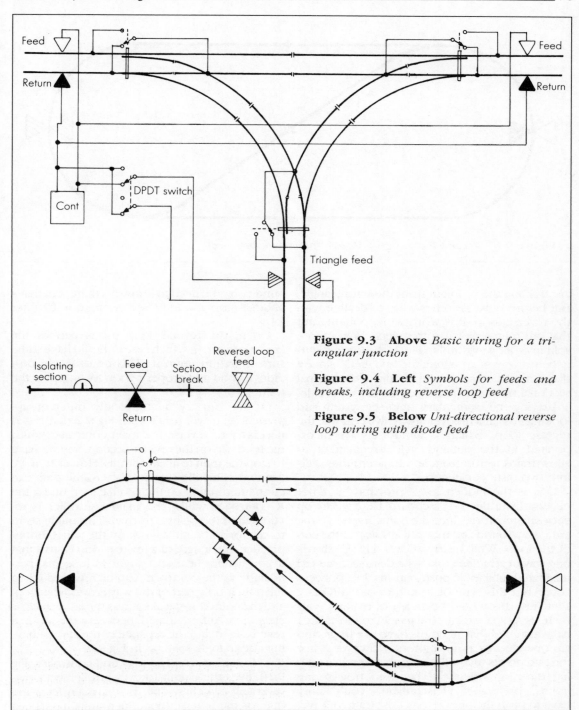

Feed

Return

Cont

DPDT switch

Triangle feed

**Figure 9.3  Above** *Basic wiring for a tri-angular junction*

**Figure 9.4  Left** *Symbols for feeds and breaks, including reverse loop feed*

**Figure 9.5  Below** *Uni-directional reverse loop wiring with diode feed*

Isolating section

Feed

Section break

Reverse loop feed

Return

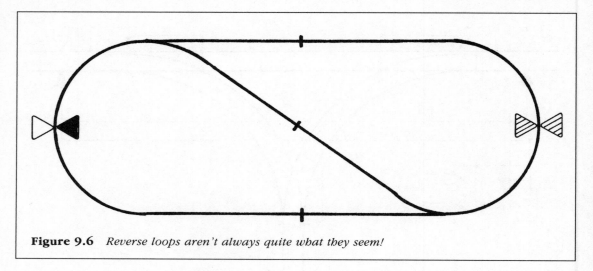

**Figure 9.6** *Reverse loops aren't always quite what they seem!*

are tackling the problem from the wrong angle. But before I discuss other ways of dealing with the reverse loop, it is worthwhile pointing out that our train set oval with reverse loop can be split in other ways, and in Fig 9.6 I show a slightly better way of arranging the two feeds, since a diagonal section across the middle of the normal sectional track oval is a shade on the short side.

Leaving the elementary train set system and looking now at a model railway, we find that the reverse loop, which is almost always incorporated in the out-and-back arrangement to allow trains to run from and to a terminus, falls into two distinct categories.

One is the hidden loop, probably, but not necessarily under the baseboard. Here we are on very safe territory, since the trains always go the same way round and they always stop at the end of the loop. Well, nearly always. Fig 9.7 shows one way of arranging this, with dead sections fed through double-pole push-buttons. I've only encountered this type of switch in old GPO key switches; this would be a case of making your own, using spare relay contacts. In this instance I have assumed that all points have live frogs, and are operated by point motors. However, since the two points marked S are only taken in a trailing direction, they can be dead frog spring points, preferably Fleischmann. You'd only have to push the button to get the train to leave.

Mind you, you need to know it's there, but that's another story, which I will come to in Chapter 14.

Often, the reverse loop forms part of the layout proper, in which case it should have some sort of station upon it. This immediately provides a good and proper reason for stopping the train.

Or we can try a completely different approach. You will recall from Fig 9.2 that it was necessary to reverse the main controller whilst the train was on the reverse section, and we have to stop the train to allow for this. However, if we use two controllers, as in Fig 9.8, the train can continue running on the reverse loop under the R controller whilst the main controller is reversed and the point is thrown. This might seem to call for some nifty work on the panel, but in practice, the length of a reverse loop is such that it is nowhere near so fraught as it seems, particularly as the controller can be reversed when the train is only part of the way around the loop, and the point thrown as soon as the last vehicle is clear. I've differentiated between the normal reverse feed and the separate controller by having one triangle solid, as in Fig 9.9.

You don't even need a second controller. Fig 9.10 gives the circuit for a controller with two reversing switches, one for the main feed and one for the reverse loop. Such units have been

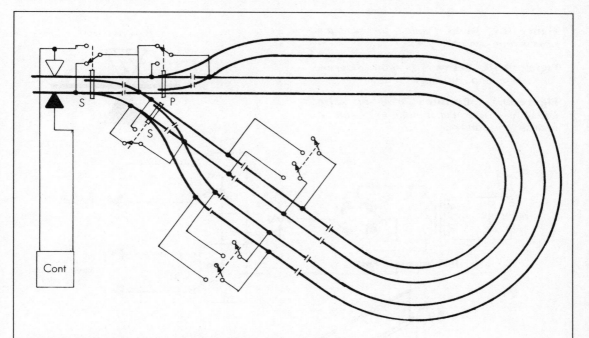

**Figure 9.7**  *Wiring for a reverse loop storage siding arrangement*
*The point marked P is remotely controlled*
*The points marked S may be spring loaded dead frog*

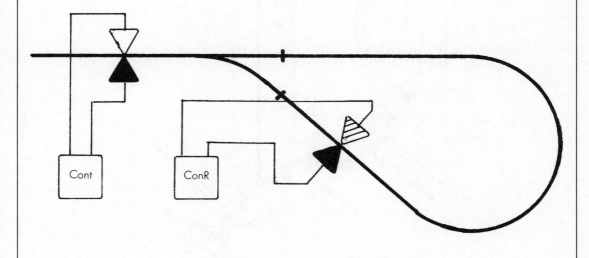

**Figure 9.8**  *Feeding reverse loop from separate controller*

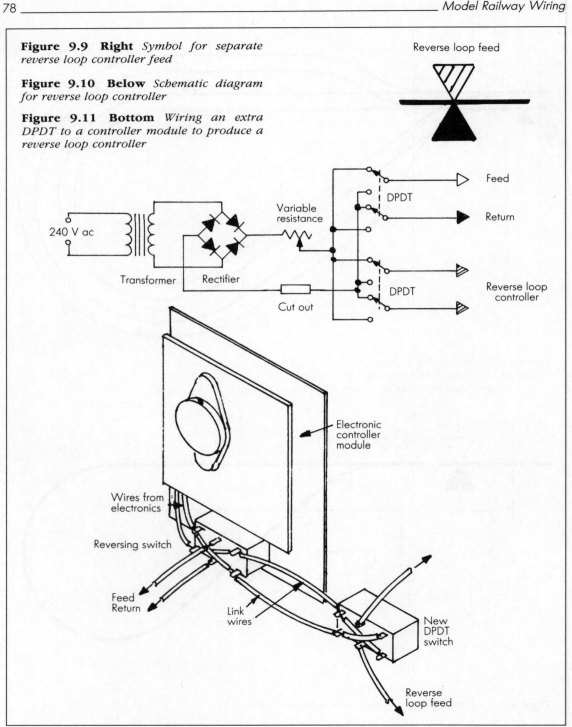

**Figure 9.9 Right** *Symbol for separate reverse loop controller feed*

**Figure 9.10 Below** *Schematic diagram for reverse loop controller*

**Figure 9.11 Bottom** *Wiring an extra DPDT to a controller module to produce a reverse loop controller*

Reverse loop feed

240 V ac

Transformer

Rectifier

Variable resistance

Cut out

DPDT

Feed

Return

DPDT

Reverse loop controller

Electronic controller module

Wires from electronics

Reversing switch

Feed Return

Link wires

New DPDT switch

Reverse loop feed

marketed in the USA, where the common British centre zero controller is all but unknown and all controllers, or throttles as they prefer to call them, are fitted with a separate reverse switch.

Whilst no commercial controller with two switches exists, many controller modules have separate reverse switches; this is the usual arrangement with transistorized controllers. Fig 9.11 shows how a second DPDT switch can be wired in parallel with the original to provide reverse loop feed. The main thing to do is to check which set of terminals on the original DPDT go to the track and which to the speed control module. You link your new switch to the latter pair.

We now return to the triangular junction, which I deliberately left partially covered at the outset, since its main function on a model railway is to link the main terminus with a continuous run. This is shown diagrammatically in Fig 9.12. The layout shown is improbable, though I have an idea something not far removed from this was fairly common before the First World War; it would have been a useful stamping ground for live steam gauge 1 locomotives in the attic of a large Edwardian town house. It does, however, show that if we have the main feed on the terminus, where most of the action takes place, and then have one or two controllers on the main line, we are able to run trains

**Figure 9.12** *Basic wiring for triangular junction layout*

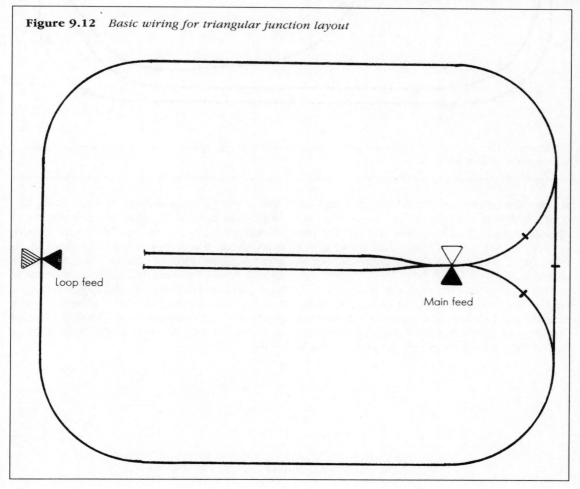

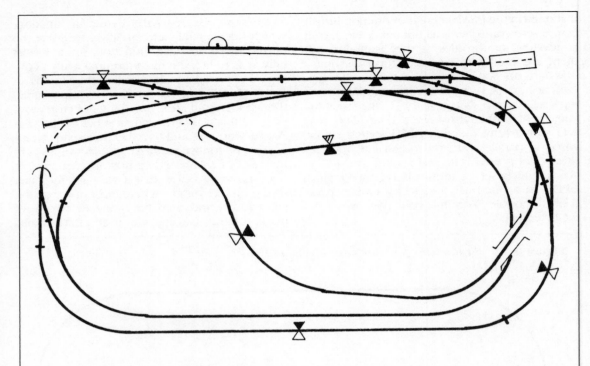

**Figure 9.13** *A typical multi-level layout incorporating a triangular junction with a continuous run. (Not to scale)*

at will without any special circuitry; although the controllers will need to be set in unison, the operator's own common sense will see that this is done, since you don't, as a rule, try to take a train into a terminus with the controller set to take it out!

This type of layout, with the terminus on a peninsula baseboard in the centre of the room, needs a good deal of space, but by introducing gradients and twisting the formation back on itself, the arrangement is perfectly feasible within quite a modest space in 4mm scale, and easily attainable in N gauge. Such a scheme is shown in Fig 9.13; as has been my practice throughout, the layout is not fully detailed, to avoid any confusion between the scenic features and the wiring symbols. It is, moreover, no more than a preliminary sketch; the original is only roughly to scale and should not be used as a guide. Anyone wanting more detailed plans of this nature should consult the *PSL Book of Track Plans*.

# CHAPTER 10

# Cab control

So far we have mainly considered a single controller, and how it affects the one locomotive we want to move. So long as the layout is fairly simple and is operated single-handed, this is adequate, but when we have a system with sufficient room to run two trains independently on separate tracks (linked, naturally, by pointwork), it is fairly obvious we need two or more controllers.

The simplest type of layout that permits independent operation of two trains at once is, of course, a double-track system. On the face of it, it's quite simple, you have one controller wired to the up line, the other to the down line and, should you wish to take a train from up to down, you simply set the two controllers in unison.

As anyone who has played with a very simple train set oval system, such as the one shown in Fig 10.1, will know, it's not quite as simple as that, because moving the up train over the crossover on to the down line creates quite a few complications, as there is already a train on the

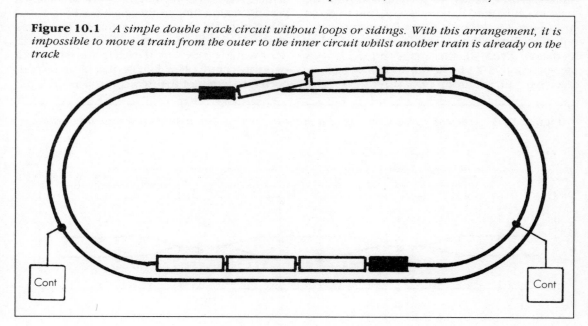

**Figure 10.1** *A simple double track circuit without loops or sidings. With this arrangement, it is impossible to move a train from the outer to the inner circuit whilst another train is already on the track*

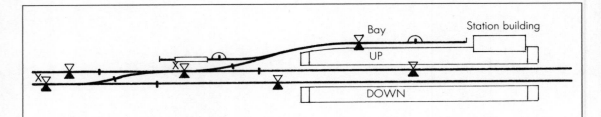

**Figure 10.2** *A double track layout, with bay road. If the two sections marked X can be switched to the Up controller, the train can leave the bay on one controller only*

line! This, however, is not something one can cure by ingenious electrical dodges, it is simply a fault of the layout design. What is needed, obviously, is a few sidings so that you can get one train out of the way whilst you change the other over. Then you need to stable the second so the first can get out and, presumably, get on to the other track.

Let us assume we have done all this, and that on the layout we have a through station with a bay platform, as shown in Fig 10.2. There is no difficulty in getting the local into the bay from the up road, and then putting a spare locomotive on to the back, ready for it to depart. Now we want to get it on to the down road, but to do so we have not only to set the points accordingly, but we must set up and down controllers to match. Even so, there is a sudden jerk as the locomotive is, for a fraction of a second, receiving current from two controllers. This

happens in the middle of the pointwork, and if anything about the train or the track is the slightest bit suspect, you get a derailment. You also lose realism.

If we arrange for the two feeds marked X to be fed, at will, from up or down controller, then this is obviated. The local will depart on the down controller, and if there is an up train standing in the platform, it can be run out of the station on the up controller at the same time. This is not only good fun, it is correct prototype operating practice.

We can carry this concept a stage further. Let's assume a layout consisting of two termini and a passing station, linked by single track. Without going into full detail of the tracks, the block diagram in Fig 10.3 shows how the principal sections would be laid out. If each feed is taken via a two-way centre-off switch, so that it can be connected to either of the two controllers, let's call

**Figure 10.3** *Schematic sectionalizing of a point to point system with central passing station*

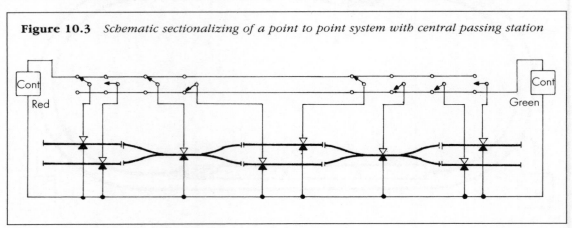

them Red and Green, we now have a cab control system, so-called because the operator is presumed to be in the locomotive cab rather than the signal box. The concept originated in the USA, or to be more accurate, it was first written up in American journals, since systems of cab control were in use in Britain well before the *Model Railroader* promoted the idea. When you think about it, it's a fairly obvious arrangement.

Before we go any further, there is one small point to clear up. As I said at the outset, all returns are connected together. We have two independent controllers, each of which has one socket connected to the common return. Now what happens when one is feeding positive electricity into the return and the other is feeding negative electricity? A good question.

The simple answer is that there is no such animal as 'positive electricity', nor does 'negative electricity' exist. What we do have is a difference of potential between two parts of a circuit, but since the two controllers are completely independent, there is no potential difference between any output terminal of the red controller and any output terminal of the green controller, until we link them. Then, as we see from Fig 10.4, there is a difference of 24 V between the unconnected pair, but as there is no connection here, there is no interaction. Of course, if they are connected, as would happen if a locomotive bridged the section break, then there is a slight problem, as both cut-outs blow. As is so often the case, although we have an elec-

trical contretemps, it is the result of an operating error.

It is important to remember that each controller must be fed from a completely independent supply. This means that each 16 V ac feed to the controller's internal rectifier must be taken from an independent secondary winding on a transformer, for if two controllers take power from one secondary, then a connection exists in the transformer and a short circuit results. Providing the transformer has, as is already the case with those intended for model railway use, two or more completely independent secondary windings, then each may be used to power a controller. This arrangement, where all returns are connected together, and each controller is fed from an independent supply, is known as common return wiring.

The original US method of wiring cab control gave each operator his own panel, with simple on/off switches connected to each section. With this system, two operators could easily select the same section, and then you did have fun. This arrangement probably stemmed from the fact that many US layouts are considerably larger than European systems, due to the fact that a much larger proportion of American homes have basements, and on a large basement layout, one could easily have three or more operators.

The normal practice in Britain has always been to use a selector switch, the centre-off changeover being preferred, since the more compact layouts we have rarely justify more than two operators. In Fig 10.5 we have our old friend the branch terminus arranged for cab control, with three DPDT centre-off switches in place of the on/off switches for the three main sections. The isolating sections retain normal SPST on/off switches, since their supply is dependent on the main section to which they are appended. The wiring is a little more complicated, but not unduly so.

It would be a trifle pretentious to have this simple station fitted for full cab control, since in practice one is not likely to be able to run two locomotives independently inside station limits. However, I have chosen this simplified layout to explain the principle, since the fewer circuits in-

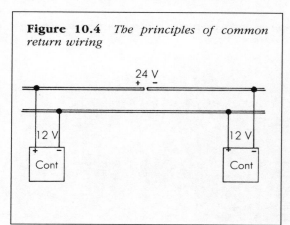

**Figure 10.4** *The principles of common return wiring*

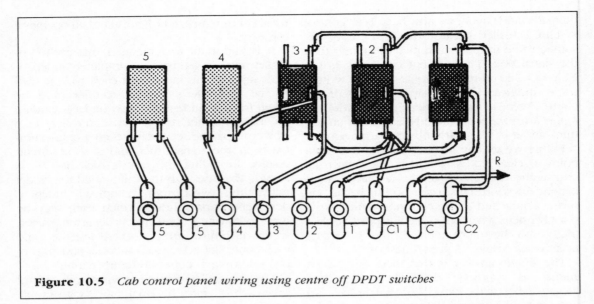

**Figure 10.5** *Cab control panel wiring using centre off DPDT switches*

volved, the easier it is to see what is happening. All model railway wiring involves the repetition of these few basic circuits.

You will see that a pair of contacts on the switches are unused. The reason is that whilst a centre-off DPDT switch is fairly easy to find, a SPDT centre-off is rather a rare bird and, much more to the point, costs practically the same, if not more to buy, since SPDT centre-off switches aren't commonly found on bargain counters. There is another reason, these spare contacts can be connected to coloured indicator lamps on a

track diagram. If red and green LEDs are employed, then you can tell which section is connected to which controller and you also find a better reason for having indicators on a panel than that they are rather pretty and impress the visitor.

If you want more than two controllers then you have to turn to rotary switches. These can be fitted in place of the usual on/off switches, but there is another approach, the centralized selector panel.

The first thing to grasp is that if you need

*This control panel comprises a geographic diagram to the left and a control section to the right, incorporating a changeover switch to provide cab control.*

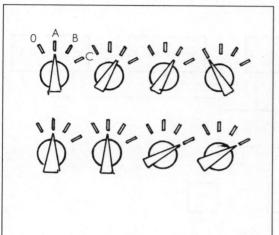

**Figure 10.6** *Selector panel for three controller cab control system*

send it to whichever of the subsidiary panels was needed. If the controllers are the hand-held pattern with walkaround control, then the operators would simply go to the local panel, plug in the controller and drive off. To obviate any chance of a controller being plugged into the wrong socket, different pattern plugs and sockets would be employed; there are two types of five-pin DIN plug, and a seven-pin DIN, to choose from. Fig 10.7 shows the schematic arrangement of such a system.

This does not exhaust the full potential of cab control, but it gets just about as complicated as I wish to go in this book. There are dozens of ingenious methods, some of which are semi-automatic and, in US writings, given such exotic names as 'progressive cab control'. Our American cousins are particularly fond of devising impressive terminology, and often get credit for devising an idea when all they have done is to give a name to a concept that has existed for donkey's years.

No matter how impressive the name, or how complex the system appears, when you get down to fundamentals, not only is it based on the principles given above, but owes a great deal to telephone switching techniques. Indeed, one method of cab control switching that was in vogue some years back used jack plugs and cables in the fashion of the primitive telephone exchanges, now found only in museums and old movies. Unfortunately, these arrangements fell foul of a rather obvious snag, the wires got tied

three, or more controllers on a layout, then it is quite large and is almost certainly worked, to a timetable, by a small group of friends. Frequently, such layouts have a main panel and several subsidiary panels. There are numerous reasons for this, the most significant of which is that the owner can run the layout, albeit to a skeleton service, single-handed from the main panel.

The main panel would contain a bank of rotary switches, which may well look rather like Fig 10.6. These would take the power from the three controllers, designated A, B and C, and

*Rear view of the cab control panel, showing rotary and key pattern switches.*

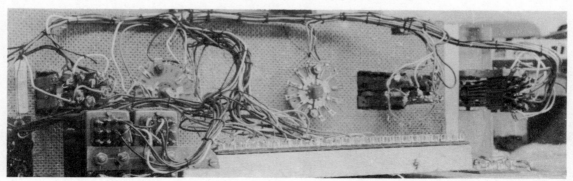

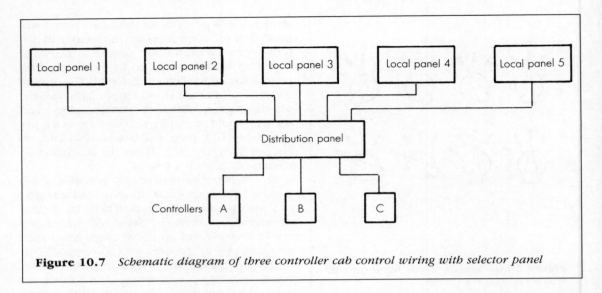

**Figure 10.7**  *Schematic diagram of three controller cab control wiring with selector panel*

in knots. I mention this as a warning; it is all too easy to get oneself tied in knots trying to devise a foolproof cab control system. The snag is that all too often such systems merely inhibit one's operation, or simply fail to work.

In point of fact, there is no need for foolproof control systems on a model railway, for one very simple reason: if there are any fools in the hobby, I've yet to meet them. The cut-outs in the controllers protect against the occasional accident, the common sense of the operators takes care of the rest.

# CHAPTER 11

# Point control

The main secondary use for electricity on a model railway layout is the remote control of points. It is not necessarily the best, and not always the most convenient way of doing this, but it is undoubtedly the most widely available method.

There are three basic systems, of which the main one is the double solenoid motor. The majority of commercial motors are of this pattern; its virtues are simplicity and, generally, low cost. Its operation is fairly obvious, the actuating armature is moved to either end when current is applied to the coil. A locking mechanism is needed to prevent the point jumping back; this can form part of the point mechanism itself, as in the case of Peco and Hornby points, hence their pattern point motors have no locking device and cannot readily be employed with, for example, points built in the home workshop. Other patterns of point motor incorporate this locking device, and frequently also have change-over contacts. Fig 11.1 shows a typical double solenoid motor. Sixteen V ac is supplied to one or other of the coils; the contact is only momentary, there is a loud buzz and, generally, a bang as well, as the armature flies over. The system is crude, the coils have a low resistance and effectively short-circuit the power supply. Hence it is advisable to provide a separate supply, generally an independent 16 V ac output from the main power unit. It is also vital to use a special passing contact switch, or some other form of intermittent contact. If the current is left passing through

the coil for anything in excess of 15 seconds, the coils begin to heat up and soon send up distress signals. Alas, by the time smoke starts rising, most point motors are ruined.

The basic wiring diagram for a twin solenoid point motor is shown in Fig 11.2. One wire, the return, is taken directly from the common terminal to one output circuit. The other two wires are taken to the passing contact switch and thence to the other output of the power supply. All fairly simple and straightforward, but for the fact that most people get a little puzzled as to which of the two wires goes where, which is understandable. It is important to get this right.

There are various methods suggested; my own has the virtue of simplicity. You just connect the two wires at random, test the switch to see if you've got it right and, if not, you change the wires over. I advocate this system of trial and error because it is very difficult, with the point motor under the baseboard, to be sure which wire does what, so you usually end up getting it wrong. More to the point, if you don't like soldering upside down (and who does) there is a very easy way of getting round this problem; solder long leads to the motor before you install it under the baseboard. For once, colour coding is useful, you use a different colour for the common return. This can easily be connected to the common tag strip, then, if the other two wires have their ends bared, it is quite simple to use a pair of test probes, connected to the point motor supply, to test the two circuits before you

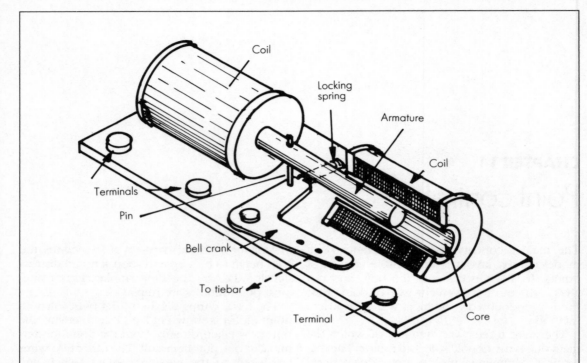

**Figure 11.1** *Typical double solenoid point motor*

**Figure 11.2** *Double solenoid motor wiring with passing contact switch*

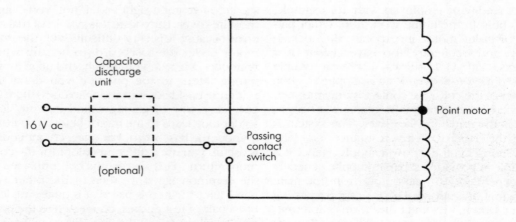

*Double-solenoid point motor with built in changeover switches.*

solder them to the tag strip.

The diagram shows the capacitor discharge unit, described in Chapter 6, as an optional extra. The advantages of this additional unit are considerable. For a start, there is almost complete protection against burning out the coils, since the unit is designed to ensure that, if held in circuit for any length of time, the current is limited to milliamps. Then, because the capacitor holds a large charge, the motor gets an even bigger kick than it would if simply connected across the 16 V ac supply.

You can use commercial passing switches, or,

if you wish to economize, the elementary contact probe. Fig 11.3 shows the basic components, round-head screws, a disused ballpoint pen and wire. The contacts are placed on a geographic panel and, to operate the point motor, you simply touch the appropriate contact with the probe. Peco produce a commercial version which is a little neater. In Fig 11.4 we have our familiar control panel again, showing the contacts for point switching.

As an alternative, Fig 11.5 shows a point motor with internal cut-out contacts, which break when the armature is thrown. This type of motor can be operated from an SPDT changeover switch, since as soon as this point is set, the relevant coil is disconnected.

In recent years a number of motor-driven point motors have come on to the market. They are all relatively costly, they all make a very considerable racket and they must be run from dc supplies. They are, however, extremely reliable, usually incorporating a number of additional point contacts, which are invariably worth every penny of the extra cost and, best of all, they operate through normal changeover switches. As with all other things about a model railway, you pays your money and takes your choice.

The third system is not commercially developed, though it uses commercial components. It also relies on a supply of powerful ex-equipment relays, such as the PO 3000 pattern relay. The principle is simple enough, a gain stroke arm is fixed to the relay armature, or, to

*Microswitch fitted to double solenoid point motor for frog polarity switching.*

*Underside of baseboard module with double solenoid point motors connected to tag strips by means of cabled wiring.*

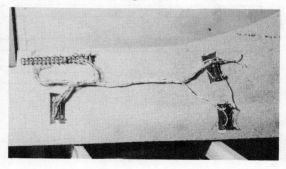

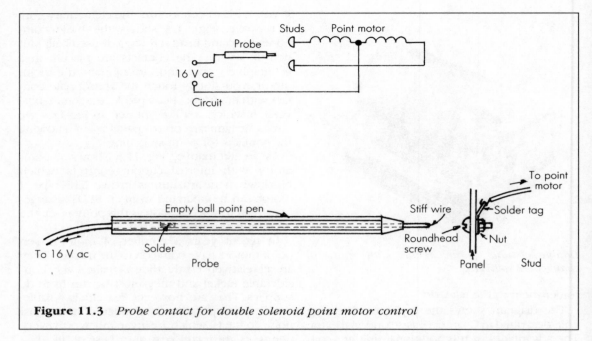

**Figure 11.3** *Probe contact for double solenoid point motor control*

put it more succinctly, a length of stiff, springy wire is soldered, as shown in Fig 11.6. The relay is mounted below the baseboard, the wire goes through a hole in the tiebar and, when the current is switched on, the point is thrown. Most relays of this pattern have four sets of changeover contacts, which covers most requirements for interlocking and frog polarity change. The system also requires a smooth dc output as described in Chapter 6.

Providing you are prepared to provide a separate 12 V or 24 V dc smoothed power supply, and can acquire a number of good ex-equipment relays, this system gives a good, positive remote point control, coupled with ample changeover contacts for track circuiting. It

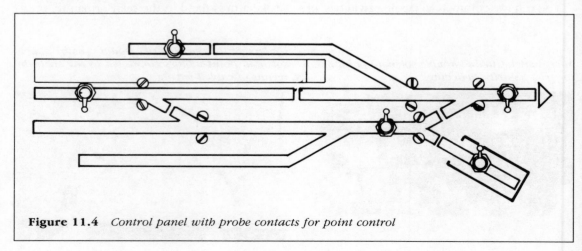

**Figure 11.4** *Control panel with probe contacts for point control*

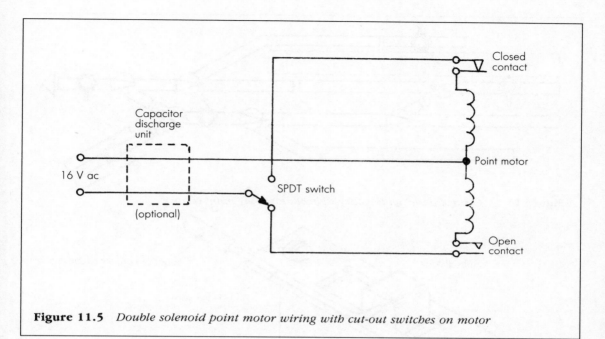

**Figure 11.5** *Double solenoid point motor wiring with cut-out switches on motor*

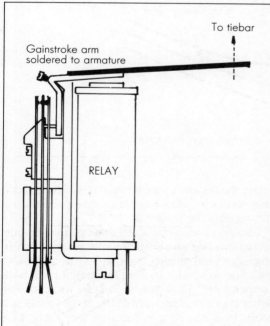

**Figure 11.6** *Relay adapted to act as point motor*

also works from simple on/off switches and only needs one wire to each point, plus, of course, the common return. Furthermore, it is the easiest system to automate, since you can select the points required through simple, permanent contacts.

Fig 11.7 shows our familiar panel, with rotary switches at the points. These can operate relays,

*Relays used as point motors. One set of contacts are used to switch polarity of the point frogs.*

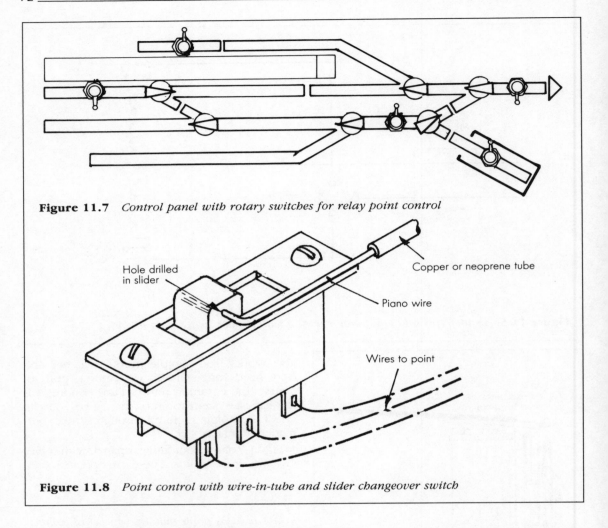

**Figure 11.7**  *Control panel with rotary switches for relay point control*

**Figure 11.8**  *Point control with wire-in-tube and slider changeover switch*

motorized point motors, and double solenoid motors with cut-out switches incorporated. The resulting panel does look very professional, since the same type of switch is to be found on many modern prototype signal box panels.

Semaphore signals can be controlled through a double solenoid, but do not need anything more than a simple friction stop. However, they are most easily operated by single coils, or better still, small relays. Once again, you must work these from a smooth dc supply, or not only will the signals hum loudly, the semaphore arms will vibrate visibly into the bargain. When using a

relay, the contacts may be used to isolate an adjacent section of track to stop a loco-hauled train at the appropriate position.

Finally, I should mention that on small layouts points can be more conveniently worked mechanically. A rather nice, inexpensive arrangement uses fine steel wire passing through a small bore copper tube. This can be curved to reach the tiebar at one end and terminate, at the baseboard edge, in some simple form of lever. Fig 11.8 shows how a DPDT slider switch can be used not only to throw the point, but to change the frog polarity at the same time.

# CHAPTER 12
# Auxiliary equipment

Whilst locomotive power, and to a lesser extent, point and signal control, is an essential part of the layout, there are other areas where electricity is used. The most important of these is lighting.

This falls into two distinct areas: firstly, the principal layout illumination, normally provided by 240 V mains power, and frequently over-looked at the outset. It is my contention that on any permanent layout, and most portable layouts, good lighting should come first, if only to allow you to see what you are doing whilst you're building the model. It is almost impossible to provide too much light, but the object should be to provide enough to allow photographs to be taken without either flashgun or tripod: in other words, as on the prototype.

Opinions vary as to what sort of lighting is best. Fluorescent tubes provide fairly even lighting, but are too blue. Tungsten lamps are more flexible, and tend towards the yellow end of the spectrum. Probably the best solution is fluorescent main lighting with tungsten fill-in, giving a more natural colour balance.

There is, however, one important considera-tion: you can easily dim tungsten lamps through commercial dimmer switches, and, by juggling with spots and other special fittings, indulge in theatrical main lighting. This is of considerable value if you intend to provide lighting to the layout itself.

Layout lights are normally low voltage tungsten lamps and, according to the manufac-turers, are run from the 16 V ac output. This is not, in my opinion, a very good idea, for although the lamps are rated suitably, they are very bright and have a bluish colour.

I prefer to run my low voltage lamps off 6.3 V ac, using valve heater transformers, which generally give at least 1.5 A output. At this low voltage, the normal miniature lamp gives a reasonably bright orange-yellow glow, and is much closer to the normal colour of house and public lighting. Fig 12.1 shows a typical arrange-ment of layout lights on 6.3 V supply, with the wiring arranged in four sections, each controlled by an on/off switch. This is preferable to having the whole layout on a single circuit, since no town lights up in one fell swoop. Certainly street lights need to be on their own circuit, whilst all the lights on the station would, similarly, be on another circuit. It would also be helpful if factory and house lighting were distinct; the danger is that one could go to such lengths that there were more switches controlling the lights than the layout!

Where it is more convenient to work the lights from the 16 V ac circuit, they can be wired in series, as shown in Fig 12.2. Where this is done, the same outlet should not be used for point motor control or any other auxiliary power, since even a fairly modest array of lights requires something approaching 1 A to drive it.

There are other good reasons for using 6.3 V, apart from greater realism. One is the life of the lamps. For a start, the very smallest lamps are not that cheap, and you need a good many of them.

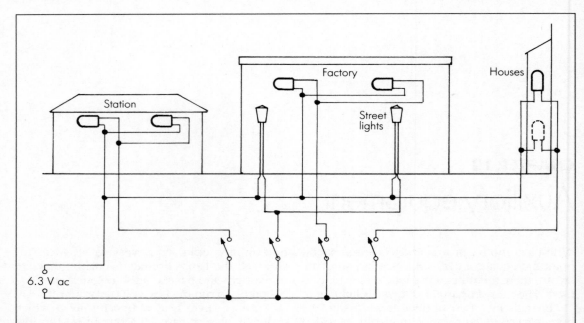

**Figure 12.1** *Miniature lights on layout, operating on 6.3 V*

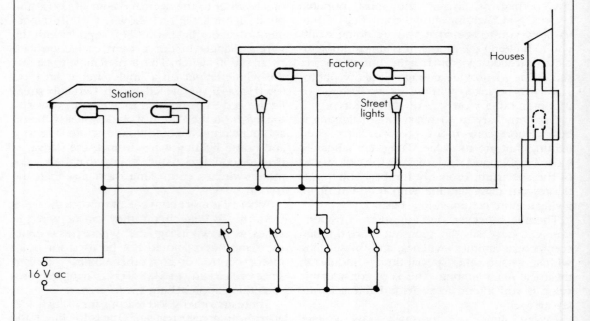

**Figure 12.2** *Miniature lights on layout wired in series to operate off 16 V*

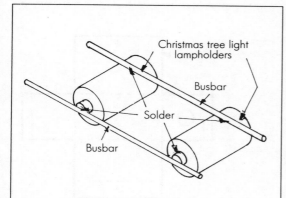

**Figure 12.3** *Lampholders from Christmas tree festoons soldered to support busbars for lighting model buildings etc.*

plastic, this is not altogether a good idea, as it is all too easy to melt parts of the buildings.

An excellent source of small, low voltage lamps is a disused Christmas tree festoon. These lamps are actually rated at around 16 V, depending on whether they are 20- or 24-lamp sets. The colour might seem a difficulty, but I have found it easy to scrape off. The plastic fittings can be split – indeed, their splitting is often a good reason for scrapping the set – and the small brass insert salvaged. This can be soldered to bare copper wires, as shown in Fig 12.3, the wires providing both support and current supply.

You can, of course, run model arc lights or more modern high-intensity lights from a higher voltage to simulate the bluer light output of these devices; all you require is an extra circuit or two.

There are two other areas where full power is required. The first is where the model illumination is produced by fibre optics. The amount of light you can get down one of those narrow fibres is small enough, and so the more you shove in, the better. As the light source can be put in any convenient location, it is no problem to accommodate a fairly large, inexpensive lamp, and to put it in such a place that you can readily replace it when it burns out.

The second is on indicator lamps on the panel,

Much more to the point, most of them are built into the model and, accordingly, are very difficult, if not downright impossible to replace. I have seen it stated that a 10 per cent drop in voltage means a 100 per cent increase in lamp life; what a 50 per cent drop means is, I fear, problematic, but it's certainly measured in decades.

Another, probably far more significant reason, is that at 16 V, miniature lamps give out a good deal of heat. Since most buildings are made from

*Low voltage lamps mounted inside a small building to provide illumination. They are soldered directly to bare copper wire passed through holes in the plastic partitions.*

*The screw connector in the foreground provides 6.3 V ac for lighting, and is connected to the lamps in the model street scene by means of the wires connected to the lamps. These are over-long, and would be tidied before the model is completed.*

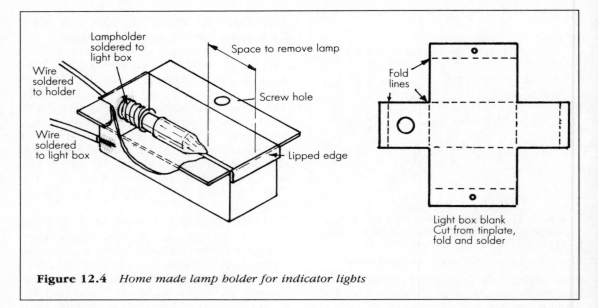

**Figure 12.4** *Home made lamp holder for indicator lights*

where it is important to be able to see them clearly. It isn't unduly difficult to replace these. Fig 12.4 shows how to make a simple lamp housing from tinplate and ex-festoon holders. As you can salvage the tinplate from old cans, the cost is nil, apart from a little careful work. Note how the exposed metal is folded back on itself to prevent cutting your fingers as you insert or remove the lamp.

One important point to note with ex-Christmas tree lamps is that they are designed to

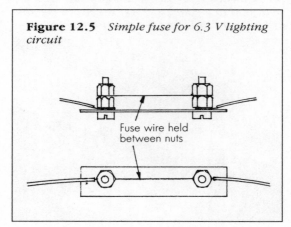

**Figure 12.5** *Simple fuse for 6.3 V lighting circuit*

short out when they blow. On the festoon this is OK, providing that one fused lamp is in circuit to prevent trouble if several should go out whilst the tree is unattended, as this could otherwise lead to an explosive situation as the lamps were progressively overloaded. When the lamp is wired directly across the transformer, then its failure would cause an instant short circuit. Hence, a simple fuse, as in Fig 12.5, should be included in the circuit. Ordinary fuse wire can be used; don't worry that the wire is rated 5 A, it will burn out easily enough on a short circuit.

I have not specifically mentioned the light-emitting diode (LED), which needs to be fed through an appropriate dropping resistor. Providing this is done, they are very robust devices, they don't easily fail and they are very rugged. They are, alas, always coloured; the first firm to patent a white LED should make a very handsome profit! I have seen some rather ingenious uses on German lighting sets, where the very small size of LEDs permits some very spectacular effects. You can buy special holders, but they are easily retained in tight-fitting holes on panels, as shown in Fig 12.6. Use acetate cement rather than epoxy, this keeps them in place but doesn't prevent you pushing them out when you change the panel. As I said, they are rugged and can be re-used time and time again.

For a 16 V ac supply, the dropping resistor needs to be 1000 ohm. The formula is:

$$R = \frac{\text{Supply Voltage} - 1.7}{0.01}$$

A number of commercial building kits, generally of Continental origin, incorporate motors and pumps to drive windmills, work waterwheels, fountains and waterfalls. These are generally made to run off 16 V ac, straight from the power unit.

Low voltage dc motors, normally from 3 V to 6 V rating, are often found in broken toys and on bargain counters at exhibitions. These may be used in a variety of ways, but many individuals fight shy of using them because of the need for a special voltage. There are three simple solutions.

The first is to use a 6.3 V supply, rectified, giving roughly 5 V dc. Most small motors are happy with this. There are some ex-equipment transformers giving 6.3 V with intermediate tappings; using one of these I've obtained a nominal 1 V dc supply, though this was more of a gimmick than of any real practical use. They can also provide something nearer 3 V dc, which is much more to the point. There is no need to use a bridge rectifier, a simple diode provides sufficient rectification for an auxiliary motor. Best, two diodes, as in Fig 12.7, allow for simple reversing through an SPST changeover switch.

The second, obvious solution is to use dry batteries, just as you would if the motors were in a toy. Whilst dry battery power for the main power supply tends to be a little costly, these accessories are only used intermittently, and so they can be run from high power batteries at a reasonable cost.

The final solution is to use rechargeable batteries, which is, on paper, cheaper, but does involve a higher capital outlay. Unless you already have the battery charger for the family radio and tape recorders, then this is best looked at as a later stage of the dry battery power, since the same battery holder will be needed whether you use disposable or rechargeable cells. A simple battery holder providing approximately 3 V dc is shown in Fig 12.8. It will be obvious how to

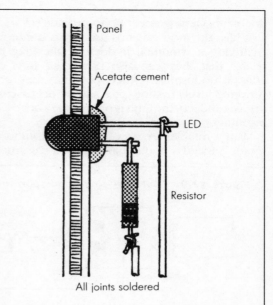

**Figure 12.6**  *Mounting LED in a panel*

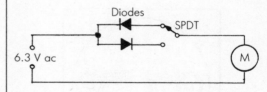

**Figure 12.7**  *Twin diode rectification for simple reversal of auxiliary motors*

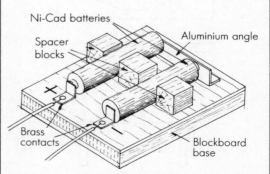

**Figure 12.8**  *Home made battery mount for 3 V supply*

double this arrangement up to provide 6 V.

Whilst the most obvious use for such motors is driving a windmill, it doesn't take long to realize that they can also power all sorts of lineside industries. Other possible uses are powered level-crossing gates and model bascule bridges; indeed, the limit is only set by your own ingenuity.

Most turntables are powered by a locomotive motor; indeed a traditional use for a discarded mechanism is as a turntable drive. This needs to be powered from the main controller, which is not so onerous as it might seem as, generally speaking, one doesn't want to move the locomotive whilst it's being turned! In due course, however, most modellers end up with a special 12 V dc supply for their turntable.

Finally, a word about meters. Apart from the test bench, where they are an invaluable diagnostic aid, they have little use on the layout.

**Figure 12.9**   *Controller circuit incorporating meters*

**Figure 12.10**   *Calibrating a milliammeter to read amps*

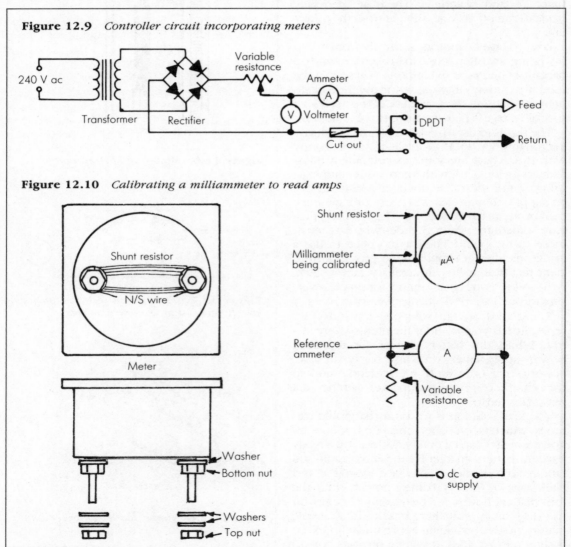

They also are a trifle difficult to wire into a commercial controller since, as shown in Fig 12.9, they must come before the reversing switch since the only useful type of low-voltage meter, the moving coil, must have dc current.

Because a meter is not needed on a layout, most that are fitted to layouts are cheap ex-equipment types. Voltmeters reading up to 20 V for a 12 V reading are fairly easy to obtain, but most ammeters read in milliamps rather than amps. Providing you have access to a meter which does read amps, conversion is simple enough.

You need a fair length of fine nickel silver wire, as sold for handrails, together with a variable dc supply – the output from your power unit is fine. The meter to be calibrated and the reference meter are wired in parallel, as shown in Fig 12.10, and then the fun begins.

On the back of the meter you will find two long screw terminals with a pair of nuts and a selection of washers. At least, you should, but with second-hand meters you never can be sure, so missing items need to be replaced.

The nickel silver wire is wound behind the lower nut; generally some three turns are needed and a good deal of trial and error is involved before the calibrated meter reads more or less correctly. As we are not involved in precise laboratory measurements, absolute accuracy is not required, which is a very good thing since you aren't going to get it, but you will get a meter reading within two per cent of the true figure, which is good enough for our purpose. A small loop off the main loop, which can be slowly twisted to shorten it, allows quite fine adjustment.

Once the meter is calibrated, the lower nuts are firmly tightened and left untouched when the meter is connected in circuit. It will be necessary to remove the outer casing to alter the markings on the scale. Small rub-out numbers can be used, after the originals have been painted out, but be careful not to bend the pointer, which will be extremely fragile.

# CHAPTER 13

# Troubleshooting

Murphy's law being what it is, model railways do go wrong from time to time. When this happens in the electrical circuits, it is time to remember the advice on the cover of *The Hitch Hiker's Guide to the Universe*: Don't panic! You only have a slight malfunction, now all you have to do is find it.

At this point you will, I hope, have realized why I have stressed the importance of keeping things simple. Complicated electrical wiring, and most electronic equipment, other than that purchased ready built from reputable manufacturers and treated as black boxes, are strictly for the experienced. Things can go wrong; they are more likely to go wrong with complicated arrangements, even more likely to go disastrously wrong when complicated arrangements are undertaken by someone with little knowledge and less interest in the theory of electronics. Worst of all, any attempt by someone, to whom electricity is somewhat more difficult to comprehend than metaphysics, to find out what is wrong is not merely doomed to failure, it is a complete and utter waste of time.

The first thing to remember is that although you can't be hurt by low voltage electricity, quite a few of your expensive devices can. So, at the first sign of trouble *switch off*. If, as is often the case, the source of trouble is apparent, set about discovering precisely what has gone wrong, and then put it right. Troubles fall into one of three categories: loss of power, defective components and short

circuits, in order of difficulty in tracing.

The circuits I have described are of a type that can be checked very simply. We used to employ lamps and buzzers, but the best all-round checker is a cheap multimeter. An expensive precision one will do just as well, up to a point; the point being that, in checking, one ends up holding a probe in each hand and balancing the meter somewhere in between. As a result it often falls to the floor. Cheap multimeters seem to take this sort of treatment in their stride, partly because the meters are less delicate, but mainly because they weren't that accurate to begin with! As we are only interested in discovering if there is about 12 V dc across the track or no resistance at all in a circuit, an error of some ten per cent is neither here nor there.

Your multimeter will come with a pair of probes. You can buy sets of leads with a collection of probes, but I find I rarely use mine. You will, in addition, need a number of connecting leads. These are just lengths of flex with crocodile clips at each end. You can buy pretty coloured sets, which have insulated clips at each end and are very useful when you want to jury-rig a lot of circuits. However, these leads are fairly short and as you'll need a couple of connections around two to three metres long, you make them from lengths of flex and crocodile clips.

I showed how to check continuity with a multimeter in Chapter 7, but it's worth showing the principle again, in a slightly different context. In Fig 13.1 the meter is being used to find

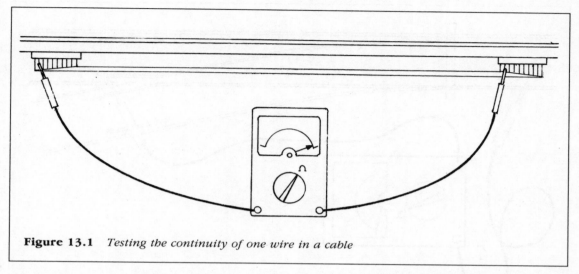

**Figure 13.1**   *Testing the continuity of one wire in a cable*

out if there is a connection between two tag strips. It demonstrates, fairly clearly, the business of probing, with the meter somewhere in between rather graphically, as the instrument is drawn floating in mid-air. In practice you may find it easier to connect the left-hand probe to the tag strip by means of a jumper cable with crocodile clips. This arrangement is invaluable when you want to alter circuits and have lost the bit of paper on which you noted which tag is which. You loop up at the known end and probe until you discover which tag at the other end is connected to the chosen tag at the start. This type of test must be carried out with the controller switched off.

In Figs 13.2 and 13.3 I show how you check continuity at points, using the multimeter set to read ohms. Fig 13.4 checks current presence with the meter set at 15 V. This can be dc or ac, the latter ensures a reading whichever way you present the probes, and hence it is the setting I prefer. However, a lot of people like to use the dc setting; it's a matter of taste.

Loss of power is usually the easiest fault to cure, since a patient tracking of the circuit with the multimeter will almost invariably locate the place where there is a break. You can often confirm a broken circuit by taking power directly from the controller to the track with a long jumper lead. Where there is loss of power be-

tween two tag strips, this usually means that one or both of the joints are defective, but there is the possibility of a broken wire. The standard cure is to cut off the old wire and put another in its place. It is rarely easy to extract the old one. Fortunately, wires rarely break when secured in proper fixed cables, but flexible leads can give trouble if the wires involved are too fine, or the bending is confined to a short section of the cable.

Occasionally, all trains run sluggishly on one section of a layout, generally a long length of track or somewhere remote from the panel. This is the classic trouble, voltage drop, which, thanks to the more efficient motors now available is less common than it was in the '30s and '40s, when O gauge locomotives routinely required upward of 3 A. The main cause is poor joints and, often, feeding a long section from one end.

Voltage drop occurs when the circuit from the controller to the locomotive, taking into account not merely the wiring, but the rails and the rail joiners, has an appreciable resistance, in the order of several ohms at the very least. It is as if, on this section, it is impossible to turn the controller full on. The result is more marked the higher the amperage drawn, hence with modern motors, which generally require under 0.5 A, the trouble is less prevalent. There has also been

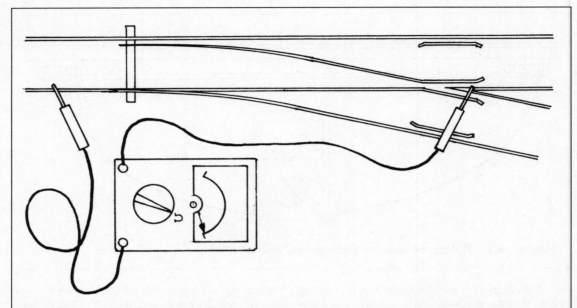

**Figure 13.2** *Testing continuity on a point. With the blades set as shown the meter should, on resistance setting, give a full-scale deflection*

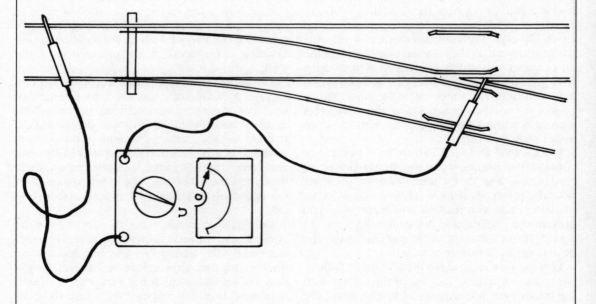

**Figure 13.3** *Testing the switching of a point. With the blades set as shown the meter should, on resistance setting, give a zero reading*

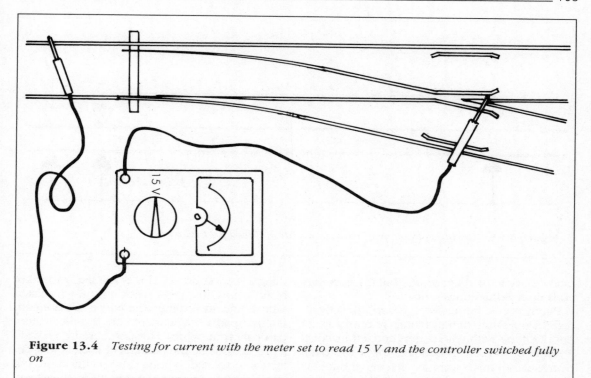

**Figure 13.4** *Testing for current with the meter set to read 15 V and the controller switched fully on*

an improvement with modern equipment and, more important still, a growing awareness of the importance of good wiring techniques. It is worth remembering that although copper wire has a very low resistance, it is not completely negligible, particularly where runs over three metres are involved, or where very fine wire is used.

Despite many claims to the contrary, nickel silver rail is not a good conductor; indeed, the metal is generally regarded as falling into the high resistance group. Brass is best, with steel close behind. However, the fairly generous cross-section of the usual Code 100 rail means that the resistance of a few metres is still low, but the finer sections coming into use today can give trouble. In addition, each joint in the track is another small, but in total, significant addition to the total resistance. Summing up, long circuits and long track sections do have a measurable resistance.

The cure is simple. First of all, you provide an additional feed at the far end of the section. Fig 13.5 explains the general principle. If this doesn't cure the trouble, you bond the rail joints. This is done by soldering a short length of bare wire between the two sections, as shown in Fig 13.6.

There is one annoying cause of loss of power that is easily remedied, but all too frequently overlooked, the removal of the plug from the wall socket. This often happens when the layout has had its quarterly spring clean, and the socket has been used to power the vacuum cleaner. This is the main reason why most experienced modellers fit power-on indicators to their panels, for, with the great majority of commercial power units, there is no indication of whether they are alive or not.

When a device, be it a locomotive, point motor or auxiliary feature fails to work, the unit should be removed and bench tested. Locomotives are easily taken off the layout but point motors are less readily changed. There is a temp-

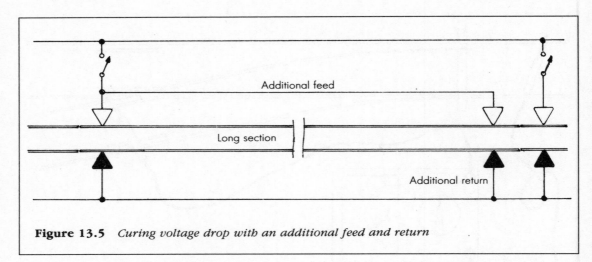

**Figure 13.5** *Curing voltage drop with an additional feed and return*

tation to try to fix them *in situ*, but this generally ends up making things worse.

Purely scenic fittings, which don't directly affect the operation of the layout, are normally cut out of circuit with wire cutters and left inactive! Naturally, they are scheduled for a thorough overhaul, but this is normally left either until the day before a public exhibition, or the next time that area of the layout is due for reconstruction.

Short circuits can be absolutely infuriating. The first thing to do is to discover which section has a short. Begin by removing the locomotives, one by one, just in case one has developed a fault. Then check to see if any vehicle is straddling a section break. This is less likely to cause trouble now that most stock has fully insulated wheels and accordingly the bodies are not conductive paths. Derailments are another cause, particularly at points. This last cause isn't always a problem, since the derailment itself is so spectacular as to lead to immediate rectification, but occasionally something comes off in a yard and isn't noticed.

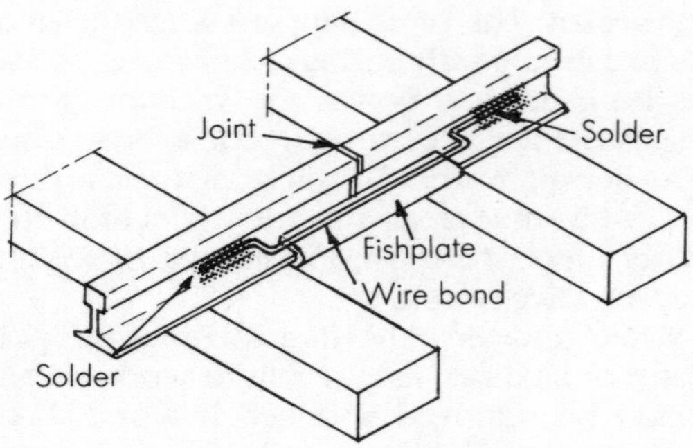

Once you've eliminated the stock, the short must reside in the track or the wiring. This is where full sectionalization helps.

All panel switches are set to the off position, and the controller is switched on. If the fault persists, it's in the panel. If all is clear, switch on each section in turn. When the short circuit returns, you know where it is.

A common cause of short circuits is sloppy wiring. If you leave loose ends of wire projecting from solder tags, expect them to touch where they shouldn't. If you have too much bare wire on the joint, once again it can come into contact. I mentioned this earlier, but it's advisable to reiterate.

Small pins and short bits of wire are frequent offenders; they have a nasty habit of falling down between checkrails and other places where opposing polarities are present. An even more infuriating source of trouble can arise when track laid with PCB sleepers is pinned down with extra long pins, which contact other

**Figure 13.6** *Bonding rails to minimize voltage drop*

Joint

Solder

Fishplate
Wire bond

Solder

pins in the baseboard. The moral here is to be very careful when pinning or screwing the end sleepers by a baseboard joint, for it is here where common prudence suggests that the firmest possible fixing be made.

Above all, check rail breaks. As mentioned in earlier chapters, it is essential to prevent the rails from touching accidentally. Since the gap is always quite small, it is difficult to see when something metallic has dropped in, or when the rails have just moved sufficiently to touch.

When a short circuit is intermittent, it usually means that it is set up by some combination of point setting. This is fairly unlikely, unless some ingenious interlocking has been devised to reduce the number of change-over switches. The moral here is always to check each installation thoroughly as each circuit is installed.

We have now covered enough ground to enable you to wire your layout and keep it in good order. This is the last chapter you need to read, since the next three deal with optional extras which, to be completely honest, are far from essential. On the other hand, providing you know what you are doing, they can be great fun.

# CHAPTER 14
# Track detection

There are many occasions where it is useful, if not downright imperative, to be able to detect the presence of a train on a section of track. The most obvious example is where storage loops are completely hidden, but there are many other instances where the ability to detect a train is useful.

Regrettably, the prototype solution, the track circuit, is not all that easy to arrange when one is using two-rail pick-up. Fortunately, it isn't necessary to go to such lengths to detect a model train, providing we accept a considerably lower level of backup than is essential in full-sized practice, where a collision is a far more serious matter than it is in our miniature world. For a start, we can ignore the prototype requirement, detection of every vehicle in the train, and instead concentrate on the far simpler business of detecting the locomotive. Or to be more precise, the motor pick-up, a distinction which has its importance, as we shall shortly see.

In Fig 14.1 we have a familiar arrangement, an isolating section, but the wiring is subtly different, since it forms a hold section in a set of hidden loops. The section is fed through a detector, and bridged by a push-button. It looks too simple to work, but it does. The detector is nothing more complicated than a lamp, contained in any suitable panel-mounted fitting. The lamp is a normal 12–16 V miniature screw pattern, such lamps having, when hot, a fairly high resistance. However, it is the nature of a tungsten lamp that, when cold, the resistance of the fila-

ment, whilst by no means negligible, is quite low and so, when the locomotive moves on to the section, for a little while it continues moving until the lamp comes up to full brilliance. At this point the resistance of the lamp is sufficient to stop the motor.

Now we come to an interesting feature of a low-voltage motor. Whilst it is moving, the effective resistance is quite high, but if the armature stops revolving, the static resistance, whilst by no means negligible, is in the region of a couple of ohms. This is why, if a loco stalls through a mechanical fault, it is essential to switch off at once, before the motor windings overheat and the loco begins to emit smoke. However, in this instance, the lamp keeps the current down and all is well. The loco stops and the lamp on the panel lights up. To restart the loco you simply press the push-button wired in parallel to the lamp, sending full power to the loco and extinguishing the lamp.

This simple scheme merely detects the location of a stationary locomotive. It is extremely useful where there are a lot of places where trains can stand out of direct sight, but it is tolerably useless for any form of automatic control.

This works wonderfully for just as long as you have the loco, or the pick-up, at the front end of the train. It poses a few problems when you have it at the other end, which is what happens when you have a steam push-pull set, or a diesel multiple unit. OK, you'll stop the train just the

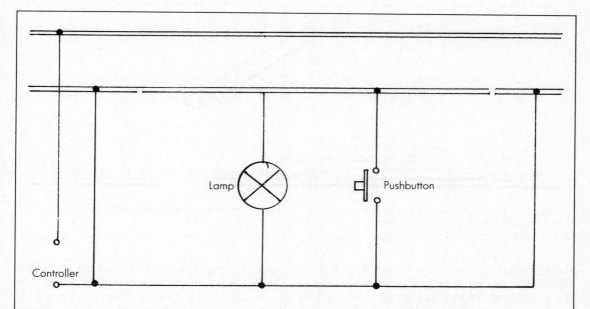

**Figure 14.1** *Elementary hold section controlled by 16 V high resistance indicator lamp*

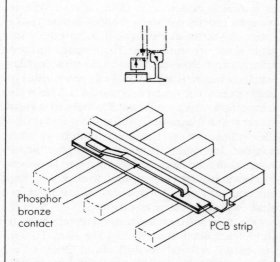

**Figure 14.2** *Mechanical treadle contact, operated by wheel flanges. This arrangement is best wired to complete the circuit through the adjacent rail which should be the return*

same, but the idea is to detect the front, not the back. You can partially solve the problem by fitting pick-ups at each end, but you'll not be able to stop power being fed to the far end of the train.

To get round this, you replace the lamp with a relay. This works just as effectively and, with four sets of contacts, you can isolate not only the detecting section, but the rest of the loop as well, light a lamp on the panel and have a spare set for anything else you may have in mind. I'll go further into this in the next chapter, since there are other detection devices to consider.

Track circuits are not the only way prototype trains are detected. There is an older, simpler device, the treadle. On the prototype it is a long steel bar which is depressed by the flanges of the wheels, making electrical or even mechanical contact as it does. Whilst less effective than a full track circuit, and open to error from time to time, it is reliable enough to serve our purpose.

Fig 14.2 shows a simple mechanical treadle which, in theory, is depressed by the locomotive's flanges, as on the prototype, making

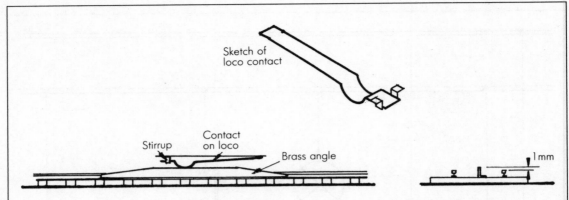

**Figure 14.3** *ATC pattern ramp contact. The circuit is completed through the locomotive wheels and thus to the common return*

contact with the far end of the PCB, this completing the circuit. It will only work so long as the wheel is in contact and the whole thing is in perfect alignment and is, in this form, somewhat unreliable. However, if it is used to complete the circuit via the wheel itself, as shown in the inset, then it will work quite well, when coupled to a suitable relay. This simple treadle is more suited to 4mm scale and smaller; in O gauge, and above all in Gauge 1 and the larger narrow-gauge systems, a mechanical treadle operating a microswitch is a perfectly practical proposition; the stock is heavy enough to work the device.

There are other means. One is the mechanical contact, shown in Fig 14.3, where a shoe on the train makes contact with the ramp and completes the circuit. This system has been used by Fleischmann with considerable success, and would be perfect for any GWR layout, where the contact ramp can be a replica of the prototype ATC ramp.

There are, however, a few problems with this, of which the most important is the locomotive contact. The Fleischmann system is simple enough in principle, a spring-loaded plunger which is arranged so as not to contact the rails. Such a device needs to be introduced in the design stage of the model, and fitting it to a finished model is usually next door to impossible. The diagram shows a suitable home-made shoe which can usually be fitted under a locomotive,

but as more and more models get full brake gear, this becomes more and more difficult.

An alternative system is an analog of the modern magnetically-operated AWS system, using small magnets on the locomotive, and reed switches alongside the track.

The reed switch is a very useful device: a pair of contacts, sealed in a glass tube, which are brought together when a magnet is passed over them, as shown in Fig 14.4. It is extremely versatile since, in 4mm scale, the magnet and reed switch can be offset in the track, thus enabling one to fit magnets at each end of the train and yet only operate the correct reed switch. This is also useful if one has a single-track system to control. It can also be mounted on the sides and roof of the vehicle, with the reed switch in some suitable trackside location. The possible arrangements are depicted in Fig 14.5. However, reed switches are not intended to cope with high currents and need to be handled carefully, as I shall explain in the next chapter.

One type of treadle to operate relays is the short track section shown in Fig 14.6. This involves an isolated section about 20mm long which switches a relay momentarily. It only works reliably on the main line, where trains are running fast enough to carry over the gap and where sufficient power is available to be detected, and is once again best used to trigger a transistorized detector. I did once experiment

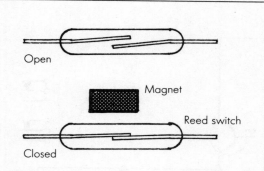

**Figure 14.4**  *Magnetic reed switch*

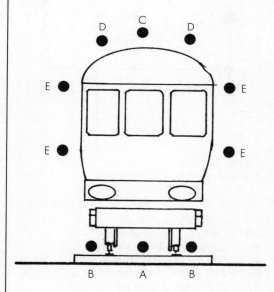

A Centre of track
B Outside track
C Centre of roof
D Sides of roof
E Sides of vehicle
*C & D are mounted on signal gantries or overbridges; E are mounted on buildings and bridge abutments*

**Figure 14.5**  *Possible locations for magnetic reed switch*

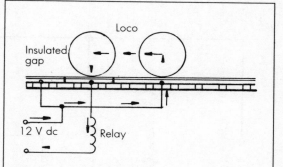

**Figure 14.6**  *Short contact section of rail, generally in return rail, providing momentary contact through the locomotive wheels*

with an extremely small trigger, made by securing a piece of metal into the head of the rail with epoxy resin; this certainly needed a transistor, as the contact was extremely brief.

Another detector, very useful in hidden sidings, is the light-dependent resistor, or its close cousin, the photo-dependent transistor. I only mention these briefly since it requires electronic back-up to be effective, but as it is the only device that can 'see' the front of a train, it is the ideal answer to detecting the point at which to stop a train in hidden loops where space is very limited. The circuit is shown in Fig 14.7, and is not a particularly cheap arrangement.

There is one very simple arrangement for dead-end fiddle yards, shown in 14.8, a simple buffer contact coupled to a microswitch. This can be very handy for telling one when to switch off, but if you use two microswitches as shown, one can cut power whilst the other lights the indicator. This is one of those ridiculously easy arrangements that do the job of a handful of relays at a fraction of the cost. Naturally, it is limited to one specific situation, but as it's a fairly common one, it is useful. One thing you should always bear in mind, you are not compelled to use the same answer to every problem you meet, merely to use the answer most suited to the problem. Obvious? Maybe, but it's surprising how many people seem to think they have to be consistent throughout a project.

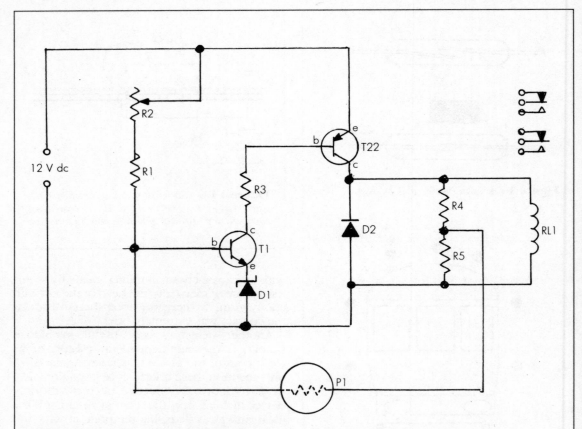

**Figure 14.7** *Circuit for light dependent resistor detection*

| | |
|---|---|
| D1 | 6.2 V Zenner diode |
| D2 | 200 piv silicon diode |
| R1 | 2700 ohm 0.5 W resistor |
| R2 | 10 000 ohm potentiometer |
| R3 | 220 ohm 0.5 W resistor |
| R4 | 1000 ohm 1.0 W resistor |
| R5 | 100 ohm 0.5 W resistor |
| PI | Light dependant resistor |
| RL1 | 12 V relay |

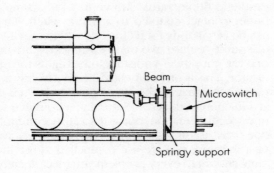

**Figure 14.8** *Microswitch contract detector at end of fiddle yard*

# CHAPTER 15
# Relays and automatic control

As everyone knows, relays are old hat, solid state equipment is the thing. Or is it?

A relay is fairly large, requires a separate power supply to operate it, and is fairly slow in action when compared to a transistor or SCR. On the other hand, unlike solid state switchgear, it can handle large currents and high voltages, and it will switch several circuits at once. All these features are tailor-made for model railway applications. It is also a trifle easier to understand how a relay functions, since the switching is

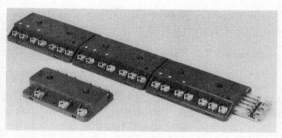

*A set of Fleischmann relays for automatic control.*

mechanical and, in many cases, can be seen working. As for speed, it's still a good deal faster than our trains and certainly much faster than most requirements around the layout.

So far as we are concerned, there are two types of relay, bi-stable and single action. The bi-stable relay is at the heart of the commercial automatic systems produced by Fleischmann and Marklin, and anyone looking for a simple way of automating a layout with minimum effort need look no further. Although no British bi-stable relay is available as such, Peco provide changeover switches to fit on to their point motors and so supply the bones of the system. The principle of this type of relay is shown in Fig 15.1.

In Fig 15.2 I show how to arrange an automatic control with bi-stable relays, using a trackside treadle or similar contact system to trigger each relay. Three block sections are shown, the train having just passed over the first,

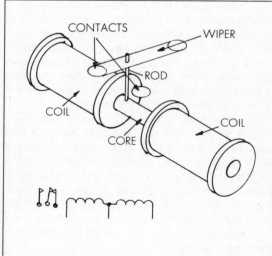

**Figure 15.1** *Basic principle of bi-stable relay*

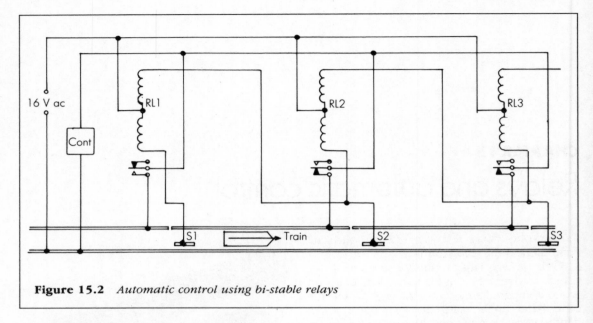

**Figure 15.2** *Automatic control using bi-stable relays*

S1 reversing relay RL1. This isolates the section behind the train, preventing a second, faster train from catching up. When the train reaches S2, RL1 is restored and RL2 reversed. This procedure is continued along the line until the train clears the final contact and leaves the automatic section.

This is the principle of the Fleischmann and Marklin systems, and is equally practicable with adapted Peco point motors. In the latter case we can use the relays to operate the signals as well; one might as well make full use of one's equipment!

Before I go any further, I must point out that there is one important provision for any automatic system: you need length. Each of the block sections must be at least as long as your normal train, preferably some 20 per cent longer, if any semblance of realism is to be maintained. This, more than any other consideration, tends to rule out automatic control on anything other than a fairly large system, or confines it to a fairly toylike system of loops left running for the delectation of viewers.

I deliberately did not include reed switches in my list of operating mechanisms. They can be used with the proprietary continental systems, which have very sensitive changeover relays, but the fairly high currents needed to operate a normal point motor are likely to burn out the contacts. It is best to use a transistorized circuit, such as that shown in Fig 15.3. Here a pair of transistors are used, connected in the classic flip-flop circuit. T2 is a power transistor and operates a normal relay RL which switches the power to the rails on and off. Fig 15.4 shows how three such detectors are wired to produce the same effect as the circuit in Fig 15.2! I am not going into detail, since I fancy that the few readers prepared to go to this length will be ready for the more advanced circuits described in *Amos*.

For those who shun electronics, a better approach is through the standard single-action relay. Fig 15.5 shows the general arrangement of the PO 3000 type relay, once extensively used in telephone circuits and still, at the time of writing, appearing in ex-equipment stores. It is fairly large, or, put another way, built like a battleship, and with one proviso, that it is housed in a dust-resistant casing to keep the contacts clean, gives very little trouble.

Its operation is obvious. When the coil is energized, the armature is drawn down to the core, the side arm then pushes the contacts over, changing the circuits. PO 3000 type relays come with a remarkable array of contacts, depending on their use within the telephone exchange and, since the contacts are standardized, a careful worker can juggle the banks around to suit his requirements.

Relays can be purchased new; the cost, at the time of writing, is around £4 to £6, depending on the number of contacts and general arrangement. It is worth spending a little extra to get plug-in relays with the contacts housed in a plastic body; this type is not only perfectly happy when mounted under the baseboard, but

is easily swapped over should trouble occur. Relays also turn up on bargain counters at exhibitions, where the prices are around half that of new equipment.

It is good practice to run relays from their own supply, either 12 V or 24 V dc. The PO 3000 relay will, in general, work off 12 V, but is normally used on 24 V. If you are buying relays new, the suppliers give the operating voltage, and you can standardize on 12 V. The supply must be smoothed, as described in Chapter 6, otherwise there will be a very loud 50 Hz hum from the relay bank, and

**Figure 15.3**   *Flip-flop transistor circuit for use with reed switches*

*D1, D2 Low leakage diodes*
*D3 110 piv 1 A diode*
*R1–R3 100 ohm, 1 watt*
*R4 47 ohm, 1 watt*

*T1 PNP high gain transistor*
*T2 PNP power transistor 40 watt rating*
*S1, S2 Magnetic reed switch*
*RL 12 V relay*

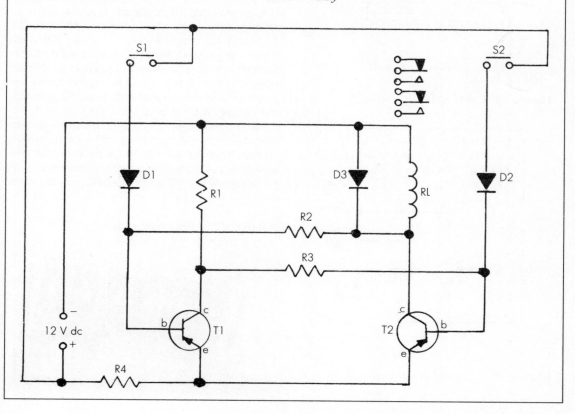

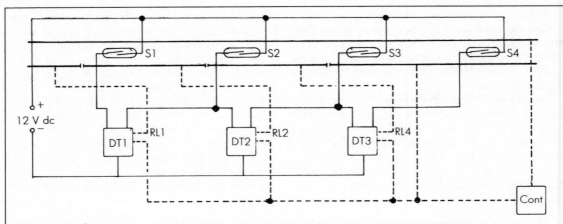

**Figure 15.4** *Automatic control using flip-flop circuits and magnetic reed detectors*

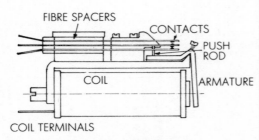

**Figure 15.5** *PO 3000 type relay*

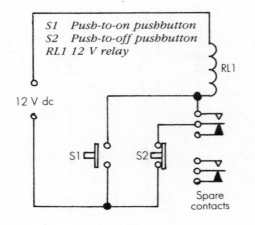

**Figure 15.6** *Latching relay circuit*

this will be extremely annoying.

Since this type of relay breaks contact when the power to the coil is cut off, it would appear to be unsuitable for automatic control. There is a simple answer: the latching circuit, shown in Fig 15.6 can be used. When S1, a normal push-button, is pressed, the relay is energized and the contacts close. This creates a second path to the relay coil through S2, and the relay stays energized, or latched. To release it, press S2, breaking the circuit and releasing the relay.

On its own, this circuit appears a rather complicated way of replacing an on/off switch, though it is the basic circuit for push-button controlled machinery. It has several interesting applications. Fig 15.7 shows a refinement of the

*A bank of PO 3000 type relays.*

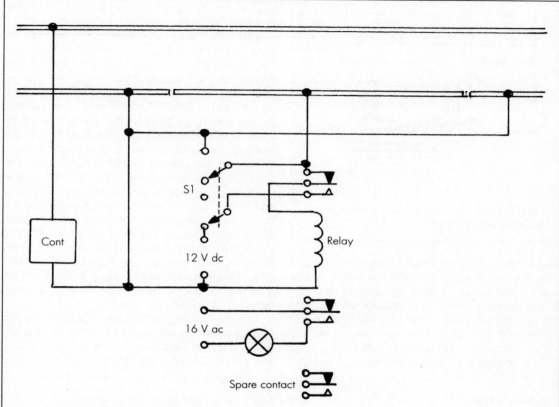

**Figure 15.7**  *Hold section using relay detection*

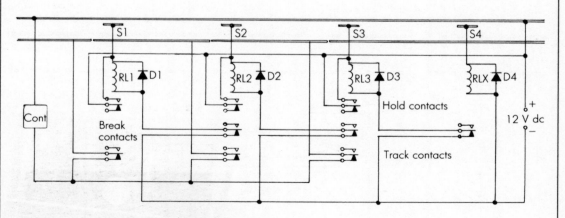

**Figure 15.8**  *Automatic control using latching relays*

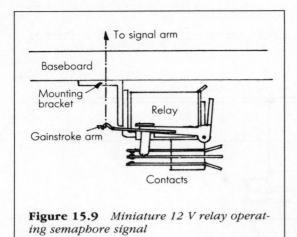

**Figure 15.9** *Miniature 12 V relay operating semaphore signal*

simple lamp detector from Chapter 14. Here, a relay is wired in series with the controller, so that when a locomotive enters the section, the relay is energized. However, instead of latching through the controller, the 12 V dc relay power is switched in, whilst at the same time a second set of contacts lights the indicator lamp. We need a double pole switch to clear the hold on the locomotive as we need to make the track circuit and break the relay hold.

Although this circuit loses the simplicity of the lamp detector, it has two distinct advantages. First of all, it is no longer necessary to maintain power to the track through the controller to keep the indication on the board. Then, the extra contact, or contacts on the relay, may be used to provide protection to the train held in the loop. I have not gone into this in detail, since the basic arrangement is fairly obvious; the contact interrupts the supply to the track behind the train. The complications come in when, as usual, the detector section is just one of several, and so the feed must also be detected through the points controlling entry to the various loops. There is nothing particularly mysterious about this, until you make the next obvious step, to get the detector circuits to switch the points so that a clear road is presented to the oncoming train, or, if all loops are occupied, the train is stopped before it dives into the tunnel.

There is nothing particularly difficult about this type of circuitry, but you soon begin to multiply relays at an alarming rate, so, unless you're able to work it out for yourself, don't try it.

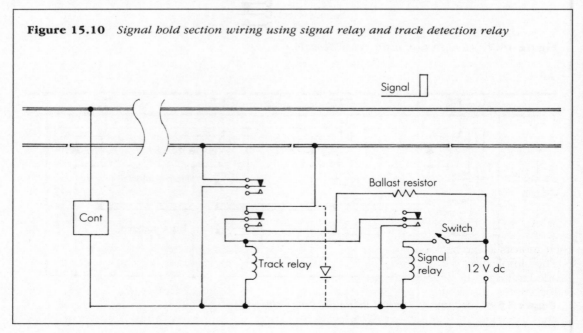

**Figure 15.10** *Signal hold section wiring using signal relay and track detection relay*

The circuit in Fig 15.8 shows how latching relays are used to provide simple automatic control in a similar fashion to the earlier circuits. Note that an extra relay, RLx, is needed to clear the final section. I've also shown the polarity of the relay supply and wired a diode across the relay coils. This small refinement suppresses the inevitable surge you get when the coil is switched off, and so makes it feasible to work the circuit from reed switches as well as the more robust mechanical contact detectors. There is no need to go in for any more elaborate electronics!

In Fig 15.9 we have a small relay set to operate a semaphore signal in a similar fashion to the point relay shown in Chapter 11. This leads me to the interesting circuit in Fig 15.10. There are two relays involved, the signal relay and the track relay. So long as the signal relay is dead, and the arm at danger, the hold section by the signal is fed through the track relay, and the locomotive completes the circuit the moment it approaches the signal. The relay now takes its supply from the relay power, through a ballast resistor of at least 500 ohm value. This is sufficient, since once the relay has pulled the armature over, a fairly low current is sufficient to hold it in place.

When the signal is pulled off, the signal relay short circuits the relay coil, the ballast resistor prevents any trouble and the locomotive now receives power directly from the controller and moves off, or, if the signal is held off before it arrives, simply passes over the hold section in the normal fashion. On single track, a diode placed as shown will allow trains to pass across the section.

A spare contact on the track relay is shown isolating the approach track. This refinement not only provides a simple form of protection, it takes care of the very rare case of double heading, and also allows you to deal with the problem of DMUs and other beasties which have their motors at the back end of the train.

The simple fact is that if you have double-headed trains, and you cut power to locomotive 1, locomotive 2 still has power and tries to push it dead. Either it succeeds, which generally pushes locomotive 1 across the hold section, or

worse still, it stalls and, if left unattended, burns out. Similarly, if you wire a pick-up at each end of a DMU or push-pull set, you'll detect the front end of the train, but it will still get power and will sail happily across the hold section. This simple addition cures the problem.

It will be clear that you can combine the circuits in Figs 15.8 and 15.10, and while you'll end up with a fair number of relays, you'll get quite a sophisticated system at the end of it.

The next question is, why not use track circuits in place of detectors? Indeed, a very elementary track circuit is shown in Fig 15.11. It looks too good to be true, and in a way it is, since it only works if you can obtain relays with coils of only 1 to 2 ohm resistance, instead of the 500 + ohm of the normal relay. A relay with so low a resistance has virtually no effect on the locomotive's speed, and so this circuit will detect any locomotive in circuit. It is a pity that such relays are very hard to track down. There is another objection: if, as is often the case, the current flow is a trifle erratic, as would occur if the track were to be dirty, the relay will chatter, in other words, drop in and out very rapidly, producing much the same sort of noise as a buzzer, and playing havoc with the interlocking circuits as well.

This can be minimized by slugging the relay. This involves wiring a fairly large capacitor across the relay coil, which holds sufficient charge to keep the armature in place for a fraction of a second, should the supply be interrupted. I have shown this refinement in the circuit, since it's a standard arrangement.

In Fig 15.12 I show how a high resistance relay can be used to produce a track circuit. The similarity to Fig 15.10 should be apparent; the essential difference is that the relay, when actuated, switches the controller into circuit. Furthermore, if a number of vehicles, in particular goods brake vans and passenger coaches, are given a very high track resistance, by bridging the insulating bushes on the wheels with resistance paint, this circuit will detect complete trains.

So far, so good. Unfortunately when the locomotive leaves the section, the relay does not drop out, since a path has been set up through

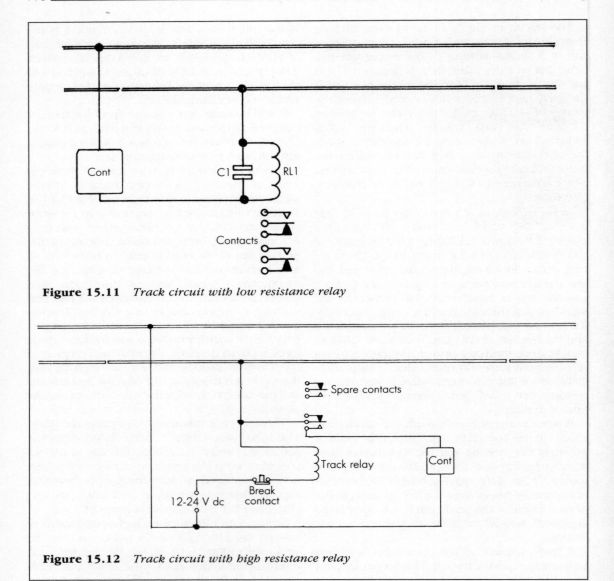

**Figure 15.11**   *Track circuit with low resistance relay*

**Figure 15.12**   *Track circuit with high resistance relay*

the controller. To clear the circuit it is essential to break the circuit, where I have shown a pair of contacts.

This is where the fun begins. In the USA, where this circuit was extensively developed, the initial approach was a mechanical interrupter in the relay power, usually coupled with a slug across the relay. It was later discovered that a diode could do the same, since when the loco comes off circuit, there is a current reversal through the circuit.

All these dodges were devised because the problem was considered as applying to a single protective circuit. Of course, in practice, one has a succession of circuits, and so all we need to do is to get the next circuit along the route to cancel

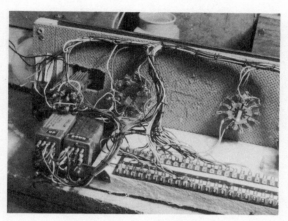

*A pair of high speed, totally enclosed relays built into a control panel.*

Before I leave relays altogether I must mention the multi-selector switch, a specialized form of relay, where a rotary contact is indexed around a set of contacts by a ratchet driven by a coil. The device was initially developed for automatic telephone exchanges, and is often called a Strowger switch, after its inventor. However, it has a wider use, judging by the samples in my collection which are not digital in any shape or form. Once readily obtained ex-equipment, it is now less common, but as a means of programming a sequence of events, has few peers. Anyone interested in automatic programming of model railways is well advised to try to track one (or more) down.

On a model railway, the main value is in ordering a sequence of events. The operations of the well-known dioramas shown by David Rowe over recent years are controlled by such switches. Indeed, many operations which are claimed to require the use of a computer can be easily carried out with a Strowger switch, since it is in effect a hard-wired memory device. It has a further advantage over electronic circuits; it 'remembers' where it got to when switched off, whereas, without fairly elaborate safeguards and battery-backed memory banks, the computer loses all its store when current is switched off — as anyone who has done any extensive word-processing soon discovers to his extreme annoyance. When you add to this the fact that a Strowger switch, ex-equipment, costs less than £10, the cost effectiveness of old-fashioned relay circuits begins to bite home.

Relays need housing. On a permanent layout, they go neatly under the baseboard, preferably located inside a cupboard to keep as much dust out of the works as possible. On portable layouts, there is generally ample room to house them beneath the baseboard. Here the modern miniature patterns, with their protective covers, are preferable to ex-PO relays which are bulkier, heavier and unprotected.

the one before, much as we do with the earlier circuits. This doesn't agree with prototype practice, since it is theoretically possible for a false clear to be made. As I have pointed out before, the only serious consequence of this on a model is extreme embarrassment should one be demonstrating the system to a critical friend.

I have only scratched the surface of relay operation. The limits are set partly by the number of relays you can collect, and mainly by the amount of time you are prepared to put into studying the logic of the system. It is, I think, essential to go about it slowly, starting with a very simple system and understanding its implications before venturing further. Be prepared to re-wire on occasions, and do give plenty of time to let the full implications of an arrangement sink in. It is, I think, sound practice to build a simple simulator comprising a short section of old track, suitably sectioned, using lamps to indicate which sections are live, and having a dummy load consisting of a wagon chassis with a 50 ohm resistance across the wheels in order to bench test the new relay bank before you hook it into the layout.

# CHAPTER 16
# Building a power unit

Unless you have good cause to be very confident of your abilities, this chapter should be ignored. It is for advanced workers only, as it deals with the delicate business of building your own power supply unit.

We begin by asking why we should bother. You will certainly not make any striking economies by building your own, since by the time you have tracked down and paid for suitable transformers, purchased the other equipment and then constructed a strong, safe container, you will have paid out about as much as you would have done for a commercial unit, and, much more to the point, taken up a good deal of good modelling time into the bargain. Of course, if you do know precisely what you are looking for and are prepared to haunt ex-equipment suppliers, you can get hold of bargain-priced transformers which are perfectly sound buys. If you have the knowledge, then you will also know how to set about the job.

Why then trouble? In the initial stages, there isn't a lot going for it, but the standard commercial unit, combining transformer, rectifier and controller is both heavy and inflexible, and as your layout develops and you realize that you need additional supplies, you soon discover that you have a heterogeneous collection of boxes connected by a cat's cradle of wires. Once your layout's basic needs are fairly well understood, you can set about constructing a tailor-made power supply unit which covers your full requirements.

At the same time, you can effect a complete separation of the 240 V ac supplies from the layout itself, and make a better distribution of the weight. Transformers are heavy brutes and, in my opinion, the best place for them is on the floor, with the lead to the mains socket well out of harm's way. Low voltage leads can be safely left to snake around the working area. However, before we begin, a word or two of warning. A mains power pack has a 240 V ac supply within it, and this is potentially lethal. Therefore, you must follow a few simple commonsense rules if you wish to build your own units.

Of these, the most important is a safe container. Although, on the face of it, a metal box appears best, a strongly built wooden box is even better, since you are surrounding the mains leads with a good insulator. Wood is a pleasant, easily-worked natural insulator, an ideal housing for electrical equipment. As a further safety factor, I would advise against a metal output panel, or for that matter, any exposed metal parts that can be handled.

Fig 16.1 shows the general construction of the box. It errs on the side of solidity, but I envisage not merely a long life, but the occasional kick and thump. It calls for little in the way of elaborate constructional techniques, providing you can cut pairs of identical wooden panels with all corners square and then screw them together neatly you can cope. I advise screwed construction, with access to the interior by removing the back panel. It is, I think, a good

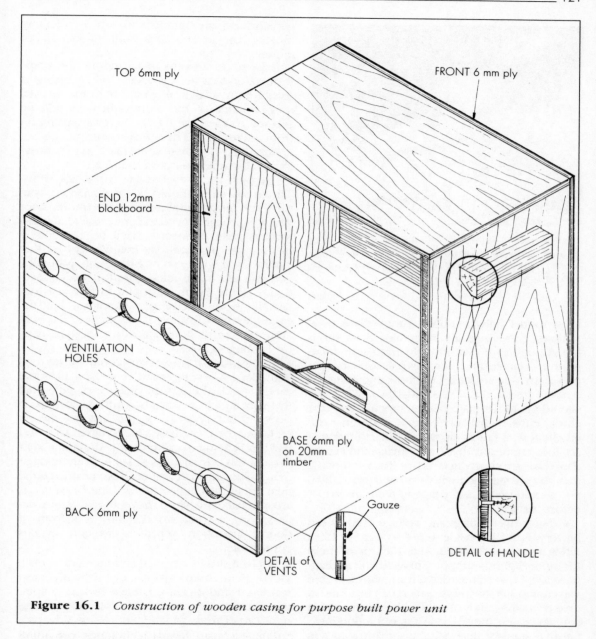

TOP 6mm ply

FRONT 6 mm ply

END 12mm
blockboard

VENTILATION
HOLES

BASE 6mm ply
on 20mm
timber

BACK 6mm ply

Gauze

DETAIL of
VENTS

DETAIL of HANDLE

**Figure 16.1** *Construction of wooden casing for purpose built power unit*

idea to make the box rather larger than you think you will need at the outset; it is always possible you will need some extra transformers at a later date.

Two small refinements are a pair of wooden grab handles on the ends, and four screw-on rubber feet. A pair of simple cleats to allow the mains lead to be wound up are another useful addition.

First, we must consider the transformers. For

*Transformers mounted on a board. The low voltage leads are taken out through multi-core cables. This set up was built into a cabinet at the rear of a permanent layout.*

most model railway power supplies we need outputs of 16 V ac at a minimum of 10 va; this is just enough to power a single 4mm scale loco-motive. Transformers with two secondary out-puts at 16 V ac are fairly common, and often the outputs are rated at 15 va and 10 va. What you should avoid for main power supplies are very cheap transformers on bargain counters with less than 9 va rating, or worse still, no rating at all. It is important that the primary and secon-dary leads are clearly marked, or if colour coded, that you are supplied with a printed key, which you should immediately tape to the transformer before it is lost.

Other power ratings and voltage outputs can be very useful. I consider 6.3 V ac at about 10 va rating a very useful addition to the box of tricks for model lighting supply. This odd voltage hap-pens to be that standardized for mains-powered valves, and suitable transformers can be found in broken mains radios of venerable vintage and in bargain boxes. Indeed, one can often find inex-pensive transformers with peculiar ratings in such places; these can be very useful for aux-iliary supplies, even though they are tolerably useless for layout control. However, as I men-tioned before, unless you do know a fair amount about the subject and are able to tell which

transformers are usable and which tolerably useless, you can end up wasting a good deal of money.

It is more convenient to mount the trans-formers on to a stout wooden base, which is at least 10mm smaller all round than the internal measurement of the storage box. It will be secured to the base by two screws passing up from underneath. The actual arrangement is not critical, but I do advise some method in contriv-ing the input and output terminals.

I suggest the use of screw connector strips. The mains input should be kept separate from the low voltage output, and furthermore, since you will probably need to connect several trans-formers to this connector, it will be most conve-nient to use the largest size (rated at 13 A) so that a number of wires can be brought in. Naturally, you will use mains-rated wire for this connec-tion. I prefer 1mm solid wire to flex; it is ob-tainable from electricians' suppliers, but the easiest source of supply is an offcut of flat twin 1mm plus earth shrouded cable, the type used for lighting supplies.

The various transformers could be earthed with a length of copper earth wire from the same cable. Standard electrical practice suggests that this wire should be sheathed with yellow/green sleeving, but since it is in this instance merely replacing the metal base of a commercial unit, I feel this is going over the top. It should be kept flat and run as straight as possible from fixing to fixing. The only part that need be sheathed is the final run to the connector. Earthing, however, is an optional extra, since the method of construc-tion using a stout wooden box is a form of double insulation, where a two-core lead is permissible.

Fig 16.2 shows a typical arrangement in plain view. Four transformers are shown, trans-formers 1 and 2 giving a single 16 V ac output, transformer 3 a twin 16 V ac output and transformer four, which is set to one side, pro-viding 6.3 V ac. This last is depicted as a unit taken from a scrapped mains-powered valve radio, and would have in addition to the 6.3 V secondary a further high voltage output, which is of no value whatsoever to us and is therefore left unconnected.

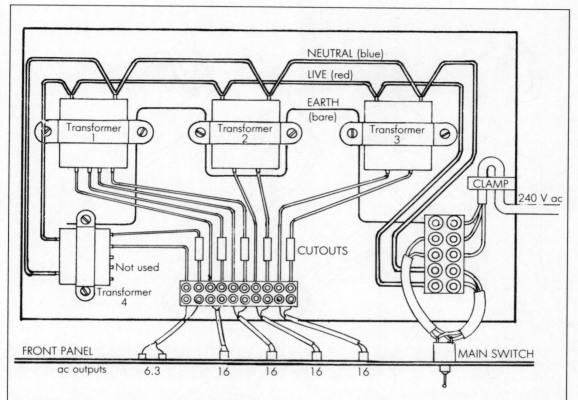

**Figure 16.2** *Practical wiring diagram of power unit. The number of transformers included is typical, as are the types shown. This will vary according to requirements*

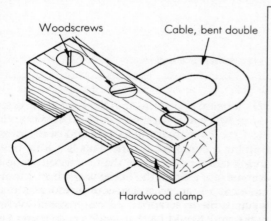

**Figure 16.3** *Sketch of main cable clamp*

All connections are made through screw-pattern connectors, the ones to the right being heavier duty pattern, since they carry the mains voltages. Never be tempted to use one strip for both 240 V ac and low voltages; this can lead to confusion and inevitable trouble.

There are five mains connectors, arranged as shown to allow us to fit a double-pole mains switch and neon indicator to the front of the casing, but before we do this, we must consider the mains lead itself.

It must be plastic shrouded two- or three-core wire, preferably rated at 5 A rather than 3 A. You will need around two metres, so that it will reach the mains socket on the railway room wall. I would suggest a maximum length of four metres; anything longer can create a potential danger

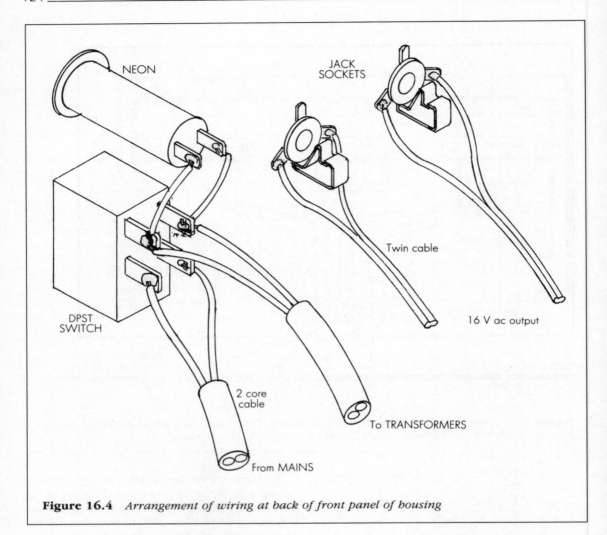

NEON

JACK
SOCKETS

Twin cable

16 V ac output

DPST
SWITCH

2 core
cable

To TRANSFORMERS

From MAINS

**Figure 16.4**  *Arrangement of wiring at back of front panel of housing*

when moving the unit, since it is difficult to avoid dropping it and then tripping over the lead. If the socket is any further away, either use an extension lead or, best of all, have a new socket wired in a more convenient location.

The three pinch screws in the connector are not going to anchor the wire, and as it is bound to get tugged from time to time, it is vital, for safety reasons alone, to prevent any strain falling on to these connections. Therefore, the lead must be securely anchored in place. Some people advocate tying a knot in the wire to pre-

vent it being pulled through the hole in the case. My preference is for a secure cleat, as shown in Fig 16.3. This holds the looped end of the wire, forming a complete U-turn. This is a trifle belt-and-braces, and far more than is customary in a commercial unit. In the home workshop, the arrangement is cheap and easy to produce and, as we have plenty of room, we can make absolutely certain. My point is that, since a power unit sits on the floor out of sight under the layout, it is open to bumps and knocks, and the last thing we want is to have the mains cable pulled out, with bare, live wires at its end. If a wire is pulled out of a mains plug top, the worst that can happen is for the plug fuse to blow. If it is pulled out of the unit itself, the best we can hope for is for the plug fuse to blow!

The final refinement is a rubber grommet in the hole in the side of the box. With a wooden box this is less important than it is with metal, but it does prevent chafing.

In Fig 16.4 we have the arrangement of the mains switch and neon indicator, viewed from inside the box. There are two reasonably long lengths of twin core mains flex connected to the poles of the switch, and two shorter leads going to the neon indicator. You need longish leads since the switches are fixed to the box and you will need to draw the transformer base out for maintenance. I have shown shrouded twin-core cable rather than simple flex, so that we know which wires carry mains voltages.

There should be also some indication of which lead is which, since it will almost certainly be more convenient to use two lengths of identical cable. A piece of coloured adhesive tape wrapped around one end is quite effective.

The neon indicator is not absolutely essential, but it does show if the unit is receiving mains current or not. This can act as a reminder to switch off; it can also let us know if the unit is inoperative, possibly because it has been switched off at the mains or even because the plug is out of the socket.

A fuse could be fitted, but as the unit is already protected by the 3 A fuse in the plug, it is unnecessary. I sometimes believe that the reason many commercial mains devices carry fuses is to cope with the less effective power supply arrangements elsewhere in Europe.

Before I leave the subject of mains voltages, which are always potentially lethal, I must emphasize that if you have any doubts at all, consult a qualified electrician. By that I do not mean the fellow next door who tinkers with his house wiring, or the salesman in the local hi-fi dealers. For most of us a sound DIY manual, written by a qualified electrician who is able to explain clearly and concisely how the work should be carried out, is ideal and is always on hand for reference. I should add that, before I start work on any mains

wiring project, I refresh my memory by re-reading my own DIY manuals.

Getting back to the unit, a further rank of connectors along the facing edge of the transformer base is connected to the secondary outputs of the transformers. Further lengths of flex take these to the output sockets, and since the leads are most conveniently paired, we can use a 3 A unshrouded mains flex for this purpose, providing that, as I said earlier, the mains supply is carried in shrouded cable and is easily distinguishable. These are connected to suitable sockets on the front panel and are shown in Fig 16.4.

There are various ways of arranging these outlets. A popular favourite is the standard screw pattern connector, which is cheap, easily obtainable, or even improvised from a suitable screw, a couple of nuts and washers and a solder tag. Only crass carelessness will lose any vital part, and in most cases this is easily replaced.

The diagram, however, shows a jack socket; these are a little more costly, but they do permit the leads to be plugged in quickly. An alternative is the two-pin DIN plug and socket used to connect loudspeakers. I don't advocate multi-pin sockets, since this power unit can well supply the needs of several different layouts in the course of time and what is highly convenient now may be less than useful in ten years' time.

The top of the unit should be kept completely clear of any obstruction, since experience shows that things do get put on top of large boxes, particularly when they are standing on the floor. Rather than make this difficult and inconvenient, I think we should accept that it is a perfectly natural occurrence and ensure that it causes no problems.

It is a good idea to fit thermal cut-outs in the low voltage secondary leads, even where current limiters are provided on the panel. It isn't wholly a belt-and-braces concept, the low voltage leads from the power pack will be the most vulnerable wiring on the layout. They will lie on the floor, be trodden on and have things dropped on them. So, even though you're protected at the panel, you can easily get a short circuit on the live side of your cut-outs and merrily ruin your transformers. The first indication you will get of this is the loud bang as the 3 A fuse in your power plug blows. This is about the only thing that can go wrong with a power pack built on these lines, but it is a major disaster by any standards.

Although, originally, I fitted rectifiers and smoothing circuits inside the power pack, today I think it more convenient to make all the outputs ac, particularly as most modern controllers are designed for ac input. Furthermore, it is more convenient to have the smoothing circuits and other fittings behind the panel, where they are accessible, rather than inside the power supply unit, which should remain sealed.

Your transformers will generate a certain amount of heat, and even inside a large box, this will in time build up and can cause trouble. Therefore, ventilation is a must. I have shown a series of large holes around 20–25mm dia, in the back of the unit with close-mesh gauze fitted

firmly inside. Fine nylon net is probably best for this purpose; all you need do is prevent accidental entry. For added safety (particularly if there are young children in the home), small panels are worth fitting behind to prevent anything being pushed through. I don't recommend a series of small holes, since it is not a good idea to have any opening in the casing large enough to allow an opened-up paper clip to poke through. With this amount of ventilation, you can leave the transformers permanently powered up, it won't do them any harm, but on the other hand, it isn't going to improve your quarterly bill for, although the drain is very small, over the course of a week it adds up. The provision of the neon indicator and the double pole switch makes it easy to switch off at the end of a session. The double pole switch completely isolates the unit, and so it is not necessary to remove the plug, as is often recommended.

## APPENDIX 1

# Rules for wiring

**RULE 1**    Take each feed independently to the layout, via a switch.

**RULE 2**    Join all returns together.

**RULE 3**    Never allow feed and return wires or rails to touch.

**RULE 4**    Always feed current to the toe end of a point.

**RULE 5**    Always have double rail-breaks where points are back to back, as at a crossover.

**RULE 6**    There should always be a double break on any continuous run.

**RULE 7**    A double slip is always a feed point.

**RULE 8**    An isolating section should be provided wherever a locomotive has to stand.

**RULE 9**    It must always be possible positively to isolate a train against a stop signal.

**RULE 10**    It should be possible to isolate every section of track, even though the controller is fully energized.

**RULE 11**    Keep all wires neatly cabled or enclosed in a cable duct.

**RULE 12**    Always keep the wiring as simple as you can to achieve the required effect.

**RULE 13**    Never let a section break coincide with a baseboard joint.

**RULE 14**    Reverse loops and one leg of a triangular junction must be fed from a separate reverse feed.

# APPENDIX 2
# Third rail and overhead

Electrified railways have been around for almost a century, and some of us like to model them. In these very brief notes I shall consider the implications of adding overhead wires or third rails to the system. I don't propose to deal with the mechanics of providing an overhead system. Various commercial products are on the market, and the system is also suitable for the serious modelmaker with leanings towards model engineering and an interest in jigs and fixtures. Third rail, widely used in Great Britain, is a rather simpler arrangement, particularly in 4mm scale, where Peco now provide, once again, proper insulators. However, it isn't too difficult to produce one's own close replica, since a small glass bead and a flat-headed pin, plus a little solder, can provide a good replica of the prototype – if you have the necessary patience.

Most third-rail systems today are cosmetic – a far cry from pre-war days when it was suggested that a Southern Electric set was needed 'to excuse the third rail'. However, the rail can have several uses. One is to provide train lighting, another to allow a form of track circuiting, using shoes to provide contact. It is also possible to operate the electrified trains on separate controllers. The third rail is taken as a completely separate feed, suitably sectioned. However, before we get too enthusiastic, there are complications. In particular, arranging collectors for outside third isn't quite as easy as it looks, since they must not only make good contact with the third rail, they must also not make contact either

with the running rails or any metal bodywork.

There is less bother with overhead wiring, pantographs are reasonably reliable devices and as the contact wire is well away from the running rails, so a lot of the troubles that arise with third rail simply do not exist. Furthermore, as most 4mm and 3.5mm scale locomotives have a handy switch for changing from two-rail to overhead, the potential exists for operating some locomotives on separate controllers. It all looks very easy, but unfortunately, it isn't. For a start, it is extremely difficult to insulate the contact wires from each other, since the model insulators are invariably dummy. As a result the overhead spans supporting the wires are also live, and hence the entire web is one single circuit. Furthermore, reverse loops are ruled out, since the common wheels change sides.

*Overhead wiring on the Model Railway Club's New Annington 00 gauge layout.*

*Outside third rail pickup on E F Colson's 1948 00 gauge GWR branch line layout. The control panel can be seen to the extreme right, incorporating an old-pattern miniature tumbler switch, once greatly favoured since it was easily available and, like most Woolworth's products of the period, cost only six old pence.*

I am not going to say it's impossible to have an interesting model railway with independent control of the overhead and two-rail locomotives. The most straightforward solution appears to be to put all sectionalizing into the common return rail, and so invert the usual conventions. This is OK so long as you are content to have one controller for the running rails and another for the overhead, though getting three controllers into the system is a trifle fraught. I can only say that every scheme I have tried to devise has rapidly become too complicated for comfort, and furthermore, I've never yet met anyone who has successfully cracked the system. As I said at the outset, nowadays both overhead and third-rail systems are largely cosmetic. There is a good reason for this: two-rail layouts can be up and running very quickly after the track is laid. Adding a third rail or overhead takes considerable time and, if it is essential to the operation of the layout, the said operation will be a long time in coming.

# APPENDIX 3

# Computers

There is a commonly-held belief that the 'in' thing is to use a computer to control a model railway, and that the future lies in this direction. Much as I love computers, I have my doubts. For a start, the object of a model railway is to allow one to play trains. Oh well, operate a miniature railway system, if you prefer it. To me, the idea of handing this over to a computer is little short of heresy, whilst the computer keyboard is tolerably useless as a means of operating a layout. Then there are the technical snags.

A model railway locomotive runs on 12 V unsmoothed, unregulated dc, and whilst it's going about its business, sends jagged spikes back down the wires. Feed that little lot into any microchip and the poor thing won't know what hit it. So, between our computer, or computer-like device, we have to put an interface. The main link in the interface is a standard relay. Or, to be exact, where model railways are concerned, a whole bank of relays, coupled to a further selection of chips.

This is only the start. A computer has one inherent fault – it assumes, if it has told a gadget it is controlling to do something, that that is what has happened. Unfortunately, a model railway is a rather complex, temperamental device, and doesn't always do what it is told. A lot of experiments with computer control have come to grief on this particular snag. However, as it is not too difficult to introduce feedback from turnouts, it is possible to control route-setting and to link this to a program which sets up the timetable.

I know of one layout where the fiddle yard has been controlled by a computer for some fifteen years and more. The computer contains a program setting out the moves to follow the timetable, and is so designed that if for any reason the operator fails to respond to its prompts via a simplified block bell, it shuts itself off and stops the layout clock, until the next move by the operator. When the layout is switched off, the computer remembers where the operation has reached. It is a very satisfying system. This computer is a very simple electro-mechanical device built from relays, a couple of motors, a lot of wood and a great deal of ingenuity. The memory is a continuous roll of paper, with holes punched in it. The layout is Peter Denny's 'Buckingham', and the computer is the 'Automatic Crispin' which owes a lot to Babbage and Heath Robinson, and little to Turing or von Nieuman.

In point of fact, model railways lend themselves to elementary computer devices. The Strowger switch, coupled with a bank of relays can provide all the automatic control you need. Indeed, you can reach a very high degree of sophistication with nothing more elaborate than a very large number of bi-stable relays, as Fleischmann and Marklin have demonstrated time and time again.

These arrangements have a distinct advantage, in that it is much easier to program the device. In the case of Peter Denny's computer, a relatively simple paper roll is employed, whilst the other systems are hard wired.

In theory, a computer program is much more easily altered. The snag is that you need to know how to program the darned thing, and whilst I have managed to master the rudiments of BASIC programming, I have it on good authority that this is decidedly unusual in a man of my age. Don't expect to find commercial software, each layout is completely individual. And don't expect plain sailing, even full-sized computer-controlled railways, which have been suitably doctored for the purpose, take several months to debug. Indeed, I recently read an interesting article by an expert programmer who maintained that, as a control device, the best computer was far and away below the most casual human for one simple reason: the computer cannot sense that something is wrong, and so blithely goes ahead and creates havoc.

Of course, if you have a fancy to play around with computers, feel free, but remember that you can end up tying a thousand pounds worth of gear up more or less permanently. Personally, I think the best way to apply computers to modelling a railway is to use simulations, eliminating the physical model of the layout altogether. You can buy, for most home computers, an excellent simulation that allows you to drive a train over the Brighton line, or, with a different set of software, over the Somerset and Dorset. This, I think, is only tickling the potential; I see no reason why a core program could not be arranged so you could drive different locomotives over different routes. Alternatively, it is perfectly possible to simulate a modern control cabin, and route trains through a major junction. I have a shrewd suspicion that the latest, and most powerful home micros could enable you to have Clapham Junction on a tabletop, after a fashion. Whether that is model railways I leave you to judge.

# APPENDIX 4

# Command control

It is possible today to get independent control of two or more trains on the same section of track by using command control. This requires special, costly controllers and also involves fitting modules into every locomotive. The idea, whilst treated as the latest thing since sliced bread, is far from new: a command control system was available in the USA in the 1960s. It had several snags, the number of channels available was limited to five, the locomotive modules were bulky and unless one was fitted, the locomotive not only would not work, the presence of 20 V ac permanently on the track ensured that, were it left there for any length of time, it wouldn't work on any layout!

In the late 1970s Hornby announced Zero 1, closely followed by an announcement that Airfix, then active in the model railway field, were also producing a system of command control. Eventually, both systems saw the light of day. As with the earlier American Astrac system, the tracks were permanently energized with ac at around 20 V, locomotive control being contrived by sending signals through the rails to the loco module. The Airfix system used a frequency modulated signal and was somewhat unreliable. The Hornby system used digital pulses and incorporated a microprocessor chip in the controller and in each loco module. Both systems only permitted 16-channel control and, since ac was permanently applied to the tracks, only module-fitted locomotives could be used.

At the same time, ECM introduced a simplified system, using the Airfix-pattern module giving on/off control via the carrier wave, but having normal controlled dc supply to the track. With this system, a number of locomotives could stand anywhere on the track, but only the one selected could move. Unfitted locomotives would run normally.

The French firm of Jouef also introduced a command control system, which, like the Airfix system, vanished with the parent firm's collapse. If you are beginning to get the idea that, commercially, command control is a bit of a lemon, don't blame me, I'm only relating the history of the system.

In the late 1980s both Fleischmann and Marklin introduced improved command control systems. Not only do these provide far more control channels, but unfitted locomotives can be run on the system. So far, so good.

The Hornby system, despite its critics, worked; I speak from experience. The two new Continental systems also work and, with the benefit of experience and developments in electronics, are undoubtedly technically superior to the Hornby system. Nevertheless, my advice to all readers of this book is simple. Forget them!

I spoke in the introduction of people using mainframe computers to do the work of an on/off switch. Command control, whilst not invoking a mainframe computer, does employ a number of costly circuits, under the control of microprocessors, to do the work of a handful of switches. I have, I trust, shown throughout this book that, with nothing more than a handful of switches and wire, costing well under £50 for all but the largest of systems, you can control a layout laid out to conform with good prototype practice in a prototypical fashion. All you have to do is to use your head, work out where you need to stop locomotives and provide the necessary isolating sections.

Command control, on a developed train set system, is good fun. Unfortunately, it just isn't cost effective on a prototypical model railway, since the worthwhile effects can be produced with simple wiring using extremely reliable equipment that can be easily maintained by any serious railway modeller. Regrettably, if a command control unit gives trouble, it has to go to a specialist for overhaul. I know of only one retailer in Britain who fully understands the system. He's situated on the south coast, and, for the majority of us, it's a heck of a long way to go to get advice.

Of course, with command control you can run two locomotives on the same section of track under independent control. Thereby hangs a tale.

Before the war, the Trix Twin system was introduced. This provided independent control of two locomotives using three insulated rails. Until the introduction of Hornby Dublo it was the only 16.5mm gauge system widely available in Britain. A school friend and I both had some equipment and on several occasions tried to run two trains at once on the same oval of track.

We rapidly learned that, unless both trains proceeded in the same direction at the same

*The Hornby Zero 1 command control unit.*

speed, a collision was inevitable. This was compounded by the delightful trait of the Trix system, the sudden stop when the sequence reverser decided to operate of its own accord. If you did manage to flip the reverse button fast enough, ten to one you jerked the stock off the track; more often than not you simply reversed into the oncoming train. Whilst command control gives better results, you still face the same problem – if you let two operators loose on the same section of rail, the end result is invariably a collision. Which is why the prototype sets out to avoid this situation by means of a rigid system of rules and elaborate signalling designed to prevent two trains from being in the same section in the first instance.

In other words, you can't use the greatest theoretical benefit of the system without contravening fundamental prototype practice. Seems a bit of a waste to me.

# APPENDIX 5
# Sources of supply

I have, so far as possible, refrained from mentioning manufacturers, and kept to generic names for components. I hope I have managed to bring home the fact that model railway electrification is carried out with standard electrical components, and there is nothing about the hobby that makes it imperative to use specialized items branded 'for model railway use'. So called 'layout wire' is exactly the same as bell wire, and is more correctly an insulated wire rated to carry 12–24 V at 2 A. Unfortunately, a lot of 'layout wire' is supplied in fairly short lengths and can be tolerably useless on anything larger than an expanded train set or a multi-baseboard portable system.

Where do you get the equipment I've described? For a start, the better model shops carry supplies of switches and other common components, and can also supply wire. You will also find firms advertising in the model press, and appearing at major exhibitions offering a wider selection of fittings. These sources provide virtually all essentials, but the more interesting features may not be so readily available. In addition, most towns of any size have at least one shop which supplies the needs of the DIY electrician. These firms either carry a selection of low voltage equipment, or can obtain it to order from the specialist wholesalers. Many large model railway clubs either have an account with a wholesaler, or a member who has this facility and so can supply members' needs in this direction.

The electronic magazines carry many advertisements from suppliers, many of whom specialize in mail order. Indeed, one major electronic supplier's catalogue (Maplin) can be found on the shelves of major magazine retailers. These firms can supply the more esoteric items and are essential contacts if you wish to go into electronics in any depth.

When I began dabbling in electronics in the mid-thirties, I discovered, a short bike ride from my home, a shop lined with wooden bins crammed full of the most enticing items. Ever since I've had a soft spot for the ex-equipment supplier. The heyday of these concerns was, of course, the immediate post-war period, when ex-government surplus was sold off at ridiculous prices, and whilst many of the suppliers have gone by the board, a few remain in larger cities.

Costs vary according to suppliers. The most expensive are the high street electronic chains, who put everything in bubble packs and so inflate the price. However, for the special one-off device they are very convenient, particularly if the shop happens to be within a brisk five minute's walk of one's home, as in my own case. The specialist mail order concerns save money on large orders, since postage and packing costs fall heavily on one-off orders.

The most convenient arrangement, in my experience, is to make good use of model railway exhibitions, where you can usually obtain the basic elements at keen prices and, occasionally, pick up some real bargains. As a direct example, I saw a box full of PO 3000 relays on a stand at the 1988 IMREX at 20p apiece. I bought the lot, box and all! Indeed, I have never once paid anything like the normal list price for a relay, but it has taken quite a few years to build up my collection.

Ex-equipment suppliers are generally cheap enough, providing you know what you are looking for and don't waste money on wonderful devices for which you have no obvious use but seem too big a bargain to pass over. It is a regrettable fact that no matter how cheap it may be, junk obstinately remains junk. Worse, when you finally get round to weeding it out, you fill so many sacks you either need to make a special visit to the council tip, or, failing that, have to tip the dustmen to shift it.

# Key to symbols

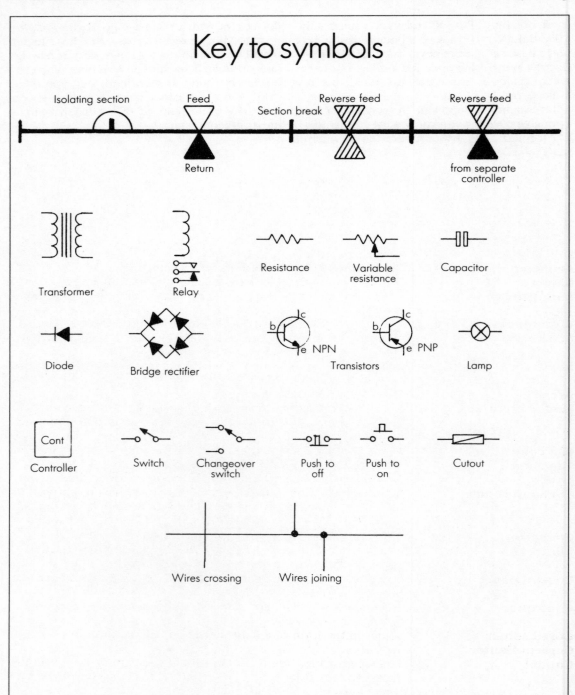

Isolating section

Feed

Return

Section break

Reverse feed

Reverse feed

from separate controller

Transformer

Relay

Resistance

Variable resistance

Capacitor

Diode

Bridge rectifier

Transistors

NPN

PNP

Lamp

Cont

Controller

Switch

Changeover switch

Push to off

Push to on

Cutout

Wires crossing

Wires joining

# Glossary

| | |
|---|---|
| **ac** | Alternating current. |
| **Ammeter** | Meter which measures current flow in amperes. |
| **Ampere** | The unit of electrical current, generally written as amps. |
| **Automatic control** | Operation of trains through relay banks, etc, without human control. |
| **Bi-stable relay** | A relay (qv) which will hold in either of two positions. |
| **Black box** | A device, generally electronic (qv) whose function is understood even though its operation remains a mystery. |
| **Bond** | A link in a circuit; often a wire linking two parts to ensure electrical continuity. |
| **Break** | Short for rail break (qv). |
| **Bridge rectifier** | A rectifier consisting of four diode elements connected in a square (bridge) formation to provide a reasonably level dc output. See *rectifier*. |
| **Cab control** | A system of wiring allowing sections to be fed from any controller. |
| **Capacitor** | A device for storing a charge of electricity. |
| **Choke** | An impedance, used to damp out ac ripples in a rectified circuit. |
| **Common return** | A system of wiring where a number of controllers, each with its own independent power supply, are connected to a common return rail. |
| **Connector** | A device to connect wires, etc. |
| **Contact** | A device for completing a circuit, usually in switches and relays (qv). Normally 'a pair of contacts' or 'contacts'. |
| **Control panel** | A selection of switches and other devices, mounted on a board, to provide control for a model railway. |
| **Controller** | A device for controlling the speed, and generally the direction of travel of a locomotive. |
| **Cored solder** | Solder in the form of a hollow wire containing flux. |
| **Current limiter** | See *cut-out*. |
| **Cut-out** | A device for breaking a circuit, should the current flow become excessive. See *fuse*. |
| **dc** | Direct current. |
| **Dead frog** | An insulated crossing in the track. |

| | |
|---|---|
| **Detector** | A device for sensing the presence of a train. |
| **Diode** | An electronic device which only permits current to flow in one direction. |
| **Double slip** | A track formation which permits trains to travel over a crossing in more than one direction; a complicated device. |
| **DPDT** | Double pole, double throw (switch). |
| **DPST** | Double pole, single throw (switch). |
| **Electronic** | Electrical circuits involving either the obsolescent thermionic valve or, more commonly, devices including transistors (qv) and microchips (qv). |
| **Farad** | The unit of measurement of capacity; very large, hence microfarads are more commonly employed. |
| **Feed** | The electrical input to the controlled rail on a layout. |
| **Fishplate** | A device for linking two rails together. |
| **Flip-flop** | An electronic circuit which will take up one of two states, and remain so until triggered. |
| **Flux** | A paste or fluid employed in soldering. |
| **Frog** | The part of a point where the rails cross one another. |
| **Fuse** | A device, generally a thin wire, which ruptures should the current flow in a circuit be excessive. See also *cut-out*. |
| **Hold section** | An isolated section used to hold trains in hidden loops, etc. |
| **Hz** | Hertz, the measurement of frequency; in practice, the number of cycles per second. |
| **Impedance** | A quality of a coil of wire which carries an ac or fluctuating current. Its effect is similar in action to a resistance. |
| **Indicator lamp** | A lamp mounted on a panel to provide an indication of the state of a circuit, or a length of track. |
| **Insulated fishplate** | A fishplate made from plastic material to provide an insulated joint in the track. |
| **Insulated joint** | A break in the track, which is insulated to provide isolation. |
| **Isolating section** | A section of track that can be isolated by means of a switch or similar device. |
| **Key switch** | A type of switch formerly used in telephone exchanges, frequently provided with a large number of contacts. |
| **Latching relay** | A relay which remains held even when its operating current no longer flows. |
| **LED** | Light-emitting diode, an electronic device which emits a small amount of light when current passes through it. |
| **Low voltage** | Any voltage below 50 V, more commonly between 3 V and 24 V. Used to distinguish such circuits from the higher mains voltages. |
| **Meter** | A measuring device; in electrical circles, a means of measuring the voltage or current in a circuit. |
| **Microchip** | An ingenious device which contains a mass of specialized electronic circuits; more correctly termed an integrated circuit. |
| **Microprocessor** | A specialized microchip which forms the heart of a computer and can also be used in control circuits. Fiendishly complicated but frequently very cheap. |
| **Microswitch** | A switch which makes contact with a very small movement of the operating mechanism. |

| | |
|---|---|
| **'Mighty Wurlitzer'** | The irreverent term for a complicated control panel. |
| **Motor** | A device for turning electrical energy into rotary (or occasionally, reciprocating) motion. |
| **Multi-core wire** | Wire containing a large number of separate cores, each identified by colour coding. |
| **Multi-pin plug** | A plug with a number of pins, handed so that it can only be inserted one way; used to connect cables to baseboards, etc. |
| **Multi-selector switch** | A series of rotary switches advanced step by step by means of a solenoid-actuated ratchet mechanism. |
| **Multimeter** | A test meter provided with probes and a means of switching between various ranges to measure volts, amperes and ohms. |
| **Neon** | Strictly, neon tube, a specialized detector lamp, generally used on mains voltages. |
| **Ohm** | The unit of electrical resistance. |
| **Overhead wiring** | The system of current collection used for most prototype electrified railways. Can be modelled using commercial or home-made equipment, but involves considerable additional work. |
| **Potentiometer** | A variable resistance (qv), generally used in electronic circuits. |
| **Power rating** | The measure of power of an electrical device, expressed in va (qv) or watts (qv). |
| **Power unit** | A box containing transformer(s) plus rectifiers & controllers; the interface between 240 V mains and the layout low voltage supplies. |
| **Probes** | Insulated prods on the end of flexible leads which are plugged into a multimeter to connect it to the circuits being tested (probed). |
| **Prototype** | The full-sized railway system on which the model is based. |
| **Rail break** | An insulated gap in a rail, used to separate one section from another. |
| **Rectifier** | A device for converting ac supplies to dc. |
| **Reed switch** | A magnetically-operated switch, enclosed in a glass envelope. |
| **Relay** | A series of switches operated by means of a coil magnet. |
| **Resistance** | A device which has the effect of limiting the flow of electricity in a circuit. Also used to describe the quality of such a device. |
| **Return** | The electrical output from the non-controlled rail on a layout. |
| **Reverse feed** | The feed, via a DPDT reversing switch, to a reverse loop or triangular junction. |
| **Schematic** | A wiring diagram where the components and wires are laid out in symbols without regard for their actual appearance or location in the unit. |
| **SCR** | Silicon-controlled rectifier, an electronic device that is the heart of 'chopper' control. |
| **Section switch** | A switch used to energize or isolate a section of track. |
| **Selector switch** | See *multi-selector switch*. |
| **Short** | See *short circuit*. |
| **Short circuit** | A direct connection across a power supply of negligible resistance, creating overload conditions. Only serious if cut-out or fuse is not provided in circuit. |
| **Slugged relay** | A relay provided with a device, generally a capacitor (qv), to delay its release. |

**Solder tag**    A small banjo-shaped tag that is placed under a nut to allow a wire to be soldered to the terminal. See *tag strip*.

**Solenoid**    A coil of wire around a hollow core; when energized, forms a magnetic field and draws in an iron or steel core.

**SPDT**    Single pole, double throw (switch).

**SPST**    Single pole, single throw (switch).

**Strowger switch**    See *multi-selector switch*.

**Tag strip**    A series of solder tags mounted on an insulated strip, used to make connections between units and connecting cables.

**Three rail**    System of current collection on model railways (now obsolete) where the running rails form the return and the feed is through a third rail mounted either in the centre or to one side of the track.

**Throttle**    US term for controller (qv).

**Tiebar**    The strip of insulating material connecting the blades of a point to enable it to be set to the desired direction.

**Toe**    The front end of a point, where the blades and tiebar are situated.

**Transformer**    A device consisting of a number of coils wound around a laminated core which alters (transforms) the voltage of an ac supply.

**Transistor**    A semi-conducting device, the heart of modern electronics. Extremely small and deceptively simple, but almost incomprehensible to the layman.

**Two rail**    The near universal system of current collection on model railways. The two rails are insulated one from another, as are the wheels on locomotives and rolling stock.

**va**    The measure of power output of an ac supply (volts × amps).

**Variable resistance**    A resistance which can be varied in value, usually by turning a knob.

**Volt**    The measure of electromotive force. Loosely, the higher the voltage, the bigger the kick.

**Voltmeter**    A meter for measuring volts.

**Wall socket**    The three-pin socket, connected to the mains and, ideally, provided with a switch, used to connect high voltage electrical equipment to the mains supply.

**Watt**    The measure of power output of a dc device (volts × amps). Note that due to quirks in ac supply, va and watts are *not* exactly identical, even though they are calculated in exactly the same way. The difference is small.

# Bibliography

The following short list of books covers all the worthwhile English language treatises on the subject known to me. It is set out in order of first publication.

Henry Greenly *Model Electric Locomotives and Railways* (Cassell, 1922).
Strong model engineering overtones, and contains useful ideas for large-scale models. Has information on early prototype electric traction.

A. Duncan Stubbs *Auto Electric Model Railways* (Nelson, 1933).
Whilst based on pre-war tinplate practice, this book describes several DIY devices which may appeal to the ingenious modeller.

Linn Westcott *How to Wire Your Model Railroad* (Kalmback, 1953).
A very practical approach to the subject, antedating the electronics era, but none the worse for that!

Paul Mallery *Electrical Handbook for Model Railroaders* (Simmonds Boardman, 1955).
A very detailed textbook, again pre-electronic. Considerable information on relays.

Paul Mallery *Electrical Handbook for Model Railroads* (Carsten, 1974).
A two-volume A4 paperback covering the field adequately.

Peter J. Thorne *Practical Electronic Projects for Model Railroaders* (Kalmbach, 1974).

An excellent practical coverage of basic electronic circuitry for a model railway, assuming little knowledge on the part of the reader.

Ian R. Sinclair *Simple Electronics for Modellers* (Argus, 1977).
A general approach to electronics, aimed at modellers in general rather than railway modellers in particular. Assumes little electronic knowledge.

R. A. Penfold *Model Railway Projects* (Babani, 1981).
One of a series of booklets intended primarily for electronic experimenters, rather than modellers. The underlying control philosophy is at train-set level; the electronics assume a fair degree of knowledge on the part of the builder.

Roger Amos *Practical Electronics for Railway Modellers* (Patrick Stephens Vol. 1 1982; Vol. 2 1985).
These two books cover the field of electronics as applied to model railways very adequately. They strike a mean between the basic elementary applications and the more esoteric field of the electronic specialist. A new combined edition, the *Complete Handbook of Model Railway Electronics*, is to be published in 1990.

Roger Amos and Martin Cook *Computer Projects for Model Railways* (Patrick Stephens, 1987).
This book provides elementary programs and interfaces for the Sinclair Spectrum and BBC B microcomputers.

# Index